FROM
ARTHUR'S
SEAT

a collection of short prose and poetry

VOLUME 6 · 2021

FROM ARTHUR'S SEAT • VOLUME 6

From Arthur's Seat

University of Edinburgh

School of Literatures, Languages and Cultures

50 George Square

EH8 9LH

Published in 2022

Design and typesetting by Ilaria Remotti

Cover images by Ilaria Remotti

Typeset in Garamond

Printed in the UK

ISBN: 978-1-7399635-0-7

ed.ac.uk

fromarthursseat.com

FROM ARTHUR'S SEAT · VOLUME 6

Editor in Chief | Abigail Flowers

Art Directors | Josephine Balfour Oatts

Ilaria Remotti

Copy Editors | Anna Koulouris

Kate Lavelle

Poetry Editors | Harry Clough

Daniels Dicks

Prose Editors | Sam O'Brien

Adam Vaughn

Associate Prose Editors | Eva Polett Lopez

Sarah O'Hara

Jack O'Rawe

Kirsten Provan

Sandeep Sandhu

Assistant Prose Editor | Ceilidh Donaldson

Proof readers | Annie Diao

Kathia Huitron Moctezuma

Paulina Schaeffer

Morgan Waas

A Brief Welcome

Dear Reader,

I never thought I would be addressing you on this page, yet here I am. A lot of things we never thought would happen did, and strange times got even stranger. This publication has travelled on roads so bumpy, at times it felt like a rollercoaster ride. A year has passed, and as our team scattered across the globe, life seemed to be getting in the way. And yet, we finally managed to bring this project to the finish line. Though these pages were meant to land in your hands some time ago, we hope the words we wrote then speak to you now.

Yours truly,
Ilaria Remotti
Managing Editor and Art Director

Editor's Note

Dear reader,

You don't need me to tell you what a confounding year it has been. We hear that sentiment over and over again from family, friends, co-workers, teachers, podcasters, politicians, and beyond. What started out as a small outbreak became a global pandemic that sunk its claws in deep, gripping society with an unwavering hold for over twelve months, requiring mass national shutdowns, and eradicating life as we knew it. You know this, I know this, so let's move on, shall we?

But still, there is a pit in my stomach that formed a year ago, as I took a Boccaccian sojourn from the city to reside in the bitter wilderness of Eastern Washington State. This pit grows not from a lack of food or an increase of fear, but from the constant barrage of clichés thrust upon the ears of everyday people: a diamond was once a chunk of coal placed under immense pressure. Every cloud has a silver lining. Shakespeare wrote King Lear while the Plague ravaged Europe. It oftentimes feels as if these platitudes are being shouted from the rooftops, but—unsurprisingly—none of them make me feel better. Maybe at the beginning of this mess, when there was only deep-seated anxiety and seemingly no place else to turn but the potential hope of divine inspiration in the midst of quarantine, I would have found solace in these sayings. But every day I spent not writing a tragedy of Shakespearean grandeur, I found myself feeling worse. So, I'm not going to force you to suffer through yet another round of trite non-statements or stand on my soapbox and remind you that better things are on the way because, for many of us, the light at the end of the tunnel is still miles and months beyond our reach.

Instead, I want to applaud you for getting out of bed today. If you made yourself a cup of coffee, or sat down for a meal, or even just rolled over and scrolled through the endless notifications on your phone, you have achieved a task of heroic proportions. The fact that you're even reading this note is a testament to your greatness, to your ability to survive, if not thrive.

It is with this sentiment that I approach this upcoming anthology, a showcase not only of the work my fellow MSc students have produced, but the awe-inspiring, deeply human strength shown by the combined force of dozens of people, spread apart by time and space, to produce a magnificent collection of artistic work. Each writer has displayed an act of immense courage by putting uncertainty aside and giving their all to a year that, in many ways, has not been what they signed up for. Each editor spent countless hours working and re-working with their writers, despite never having met most in person. This anthology has been produced not only with the passion of young artists, but the profound sense of compassion that comes with trekking through sludge and muck together, even though we may be physically apart.

I am deeply proud of the work we have produced. I am immensely grateful for these fervent disciples of storytelling. I am simply in awe at the effort and expertise showcased in these pages and honored that I was given the opportunity to put it together.

Besides, who really liked King Lear, anyway?

With regards,
Margaret Abigail Flowers
Editor-in-Chief

Foreword

In these Unprecedented Times....

Well, we've all heard enough about that. But this year's students on the University of Edinburgh's MSc in Creative Writing deserve kudos and chocolates for accomplishing such incredible results in difficult circumstances – online learning, restricted access to library and other resources, physical isolation, and a lack of so many opportunities that make student life fun. It's easy to remind ourselves that Shakespeare wrote King Lear during a period when London theatres were closed due to plague, but did Shakespeare ever have to deal with Zoom refusing to acknowledge his external microphone?

Even without the extenuating circumstances, this anthology is an incredible accomplishment. We encourage our students to follow their own paths and support each of them to develop their individual voices and visions. One of the joys of this showcase anthology is the range of approaches, styles, and subjects you will encounter, with new writers from across the globe writing out of a diverse range of cultures.

We've been fortunate to work with a stellar cohort of emerging writers this year. Please take the time to savour their prose and poetry, and marvel at how creativity flourishes in lockdown.

Best wishes,
Tracey S. Rosenberg, Writer in Residence
Jane Alexander, MSc Programme Director

INDEX

PROSE

POETRY

ART

CONTENT NOTE

Please be advised: individual pieces within this collection contain topics and themes that may be triggering for certain audiences, including offensive language, sexual activity, violence, domestic abuse, war, mental illness, intrusive thoughts, homelessness, suicide, and death.

No Sense Crying

Elise Le Bihan

Katie knew two things. One: her soon to be in-laws were less than an hour away. Two: At the speed the snow was falling outside there was no store in their right mind still open. Oh, and C: She was screwed.

Georgie's head was heavy against Katie's arm as she walked to the cot in the sitting room. Catching a glance of herself in the mirror over the mantlepiece, the carnage of the past hour was evident in the spit-up, diaper, and tear stains across her old NYU tee. Katie readjusted her sleeping son, examining her filthy hair, brown roots now nearly reaching her ears. *So much for being a natural blonde.* She looked more like she had just woken up in the dumpster of a Wendy's parking lot than someone on the verge of meeting her future in-laws. She could almost hear herself now: *Hello! It's lovely to meet you. I'm your darling son's new fiancée. Yes, the one with a baby from another man, her best friend. Yes, that would be me.* Cue the playful laugh. *Would you care for some more wine?*

After putting Georgie down and praying that he would stay as she preferred him – *asleep* – she squinted at the clock on the oven door in the kitchen. Was that a five or a six? Did she have time for a shower? Katie ran into the bathroom and rummaged through the drawers trying to find an eyebrow pencil, some concealer, her dignity, anything.

The phone rang. She poked her head back into the living room to pick it up from a nearby end table, laying it face up on the sink. She clicked the speaker.

'This is Katie.'

'So, are they on their way yet?'

Jerry. She could almost see him on the other side of the phone: salt-and-pepper hair gelled back sitting in his leather armchair, wearing a tasteful knit cardigan over a dry-cleaned dress shirt, nursing a whisky on the rocks.

'I dunno what I'm going to do.' Katie leaned in close over the sink, mouth half-open as she did her mascara. 'I'm going back to work next week and I had to get everything ready for the sitter and...' She breathed in sharply as she felt something cold against her stomach. The sink was wet. 'How's Paul?'

'Don't know.' Jerry's voice was slow. 'I woke up and... well... didn't even forget a phone charger or a sock. It's all gone.'

Katie froze.

'Oh Jerry, I'm so sorry... What happened? How are—'

'Do you know what you're wearing? What are you making?' he cut her off.

Katie pulled a piece of toilet paper and ran it under the tap before trying to fix her eyeliner. 'I don't know. I fell asleep when I put the baby down for a nap. What do you think they'll say to sweats and take-out?'

'Honey. They're from Connecticut and have a house in Cape Cod. This isn't *our* New England, this is *bougie* New England, okay? They're going to be coming in there and asking you *where do you summer?* and *where did you moor your second biggest yacht?*'

'I know, I know. It's just that Tom does all the cooking, and I don't actually fit into this little housewife role. I'm more of a works-9-to-5-and-picks-up-pizza-on-the-way-home kind of mom, not a stay-at-home-apron-wearing-cookies-fresh-out-of-the-oven sort of person.'

'Just open your fridge and tell me what you have.' And there it was. The moment when Jerry decided he was taking charge, just like he did on their nights out when they were still at NYU.

Katie stepped back from the mirror to admire her handiwork. All in all, it could be worse. She did look a bit perkier, more awake. Sure, the bags under her eyes were still there, but they hadn't gone in over a year, not since the baby. Feeling as though she had just donned chainmail and armor, Katie entered the kitchen. She was starting to feel more like herself. *It's going to be fine. You're not going to screw up, you're not going to screw up, you're not going to screw up. For God's sake woman you already have a baby with another man. What's the worst that can happen?*

Katie shivered as she stood in front of the open fridge, her wet t-shirt reminding her that concealer wasn't going to erase the fact she was still covered in barf stains. She tried to picture her closet as she scanned the fridge. But seeing as nothing fit anymore...

'Um... we have potatoes, bacon, some kind of fish?'

'Is it haddock? Or cod?'

'Hang on, let me check. Tom bought it over the weekend.' Katie pulled out the slimy white fish. After poking the plastic film and examining the indent her finger had made in the limp flesh, she flipped it over to read the Hannaford label on the back.

'Um, yeah. It's haddock.'

'Do you have milk and butter or some cream, ideally?'

'I think so... hang on.' Katie put the phone onto the counter as she pushed the glass containers around in her fridge. 'Tom has this new thing where he likes to put everything in glass bottles. He keeps saying he can taste the microplastics.' She yelled over the clinking of the bottles. Katie got on her tip-toes and reached behind a jar full of what looked like a criminal DIY attempt at kombucha, for a white liquid in a glass jar with a blue lid.

'Do you have milk, yes or no?' Jerry's impatient voice snapped from the other end of the line.

She swirled it around and lifted it to the light.

'Yes.'

'Good, you're making chowder.'

Katie closed the fridge.

'You think I *look* like I know how to make chowder?'

'Shut up and start peeling the potatoes.' The voice from the phone on the counter ordered. 'Trust me. You're going to wow them with a traditional recipe.' Katie pulled open drawers desperately looking for the peeler.

'I'm trusting you, Jerry. I'm trusting you.'

By the time Tom's station wagon had managed to drag itself up the driveway without sliding back into the lane, Katie was dressed, and re-dressed (Georgie made sure to spit up on the first outfit). The smell of haddock was gently wafting through the kitchen and into the dining room where the table was laid with matching napkins and all. It was very adult.

'Oh god, they're here,' Katie whispered into the phone from the kitchen window as she watched a formidable woman in her sixties step out of the passenger-side of the car.

'Don't worry,' Jerry whispered in her ear. 'Now, you just leave it on low until you eat and *no problemo*. You added the pepper like I told you? And a pinch of salt, not too much - you won't need it with the salt pork and the fish.'

'Yes. Yes.' Katie smoothed her hair and checked her teeth for lipstick in the dark window. In the reflection, she saw her breast pump lying on the counter and quickly shoved it in the nearest cupboard.

Jerry laughed and she could hear him pretending to cry. 'My baby's all grown up. Meeting Tommy boy's parents for the first time.'

'Don't be mean.' A smile pulled at the edge of Katie's lips.

'No, seriously. I'm happy for you honey, truly. You two make such a *lovely, traditional, happy* little couple.'

Katie walked into the dining room with the baby monitor and tucked it behind some flowers on the table. She made sure the volume was on. *No need to look like a completely incompetent parent.*

There was a shuffle at the door and Katie heard it being opened. Sharp winter air pushed its way inside as voices echoed down the hall.

'I gotta go,' Katie whispered.

'Good luck, honey. You're going to be fine.'

And she was, at first.

After putting the phone down on the counter, Katie greeted Mr. and Mrs. – *Please, call us Anne and Greg* – Thompson, with grace, poise, and well-concealed acid reflux.

As if on cue, Georgie's cries soon echoed through the monitor and Katie flashed her most brilliant smile before walking upstairs to fetch her son. Katie saw Georgie's tear-stained face. She pulled him into her arms and he tucked his head into her neck.

'You've only been in here half an hour, buddy. No need to be so dramatic,' Katie whispered, placing a soft kiss on his warm head. Voices rose up the stairs and Katie paused on the top landing.

'Have you even met him yet? *The father?*'

'Yes, Mother. Ages ago. How many times do I have to—'

'As long as you're sure! I only want you to be happy, darling.'

'Then drop it. Please.'

Well, that was to be expected. Katie took a deep breath. She kissed Georgie's head once more, for good luck. *Here goes nothing.* But Katie should have known better than to worry about Georgie. She had only to go down the stairs before he was all smiles and happy gurgles in the arms of his soon-to-be grandparents. Tom was so over the moon to have them all together he kept re-telling the same stories and Katie soon felt like she was in one of those cheesy TV holiday movies.

It wasn't until they had all tried the chowder and compliments had been given to the chef that a fussing Georgie prompted Katie to rise from the table to get his bottle from the fridge.

'But didn't you realize his name was going to be Tom Thompson when you named him?' Katie laughed.

'Of course. Everyone told us: the nurses and the doctors. They even sent up this man we didn't know, who told us his name was Fred Fredrickson and he'd hated it his whole life!' Anne was laughing and Katie saw there was a tinge of pink in her cheeks from the white wine.

'And even that didn't stop you?' Tom laughed. He caught Katie's eye and winked as she walked past him.

'I always wanted a boy named Tom. And I said to myself: I'm the mother. I get to decide.'

'Hear, hear!' Katie shouted back from the kitchen.

They all laughed. As she opened the fridge, Katie felt the smile slip from her lips. The baby's bottle was only a quarter full. She stuck it into the microwave before going back to poke around the fridge for more milk. The bottles clinked as she pushed them aside, trying to get to the back.

'Babe?' she called to the dining room. 'Where's the baby's milk?'

'It's in the jar with the blue lid!'

'What do you mean *jar*? Do they still get milk delivered up here?' Katie heard Greg ask, clearly confused.

Katie was only half listening as Tom launched into his micro-plastic bottle theory. She pushed the bottles of orange juice and water, moved around the containers of tomatoes and onions. She didn't see any blue lids anywhere. Clink. Clink. Clink. Shivering slightly, she closed the fridge. And then she saw it, the glass bottle with the blue lid, lying in the sink with the potato peels she hadn't managed to throw into the trash before they had arrived. Empty.

'What did you put in this chowder, Katie? It's amazing!' Anne's voice came to her like in a dream. Her words didn't make sense.

And then the nausea hit. Katie opened the fridge slowly and faced the wall of glass. She turned and looked at the empty bottle in the sink. The milk in the fridge, the one with the blue cap, *oh god.*

The microwave dinged. Katie took Georgie's bottle out and nearly dropped it. She had left it in for far too long. Cursing under her breath, Katie ran her throbbing fingers under cold water, mind racing, trying to stop the wave of panic from engulfing her. What was she going to do? Should she tell them? What could she even say? *I'm glad you've been enjoying my soup but I'm sorry to tell you that I'm an idiot and accidentally used my own breast milk as a substitute so if you'll excuse me, I'm going to just throw this out and we can order Domino's instead. My bad?*

She'd just met these people, and she was already at a disadvantage. She knew she wasn't exactly what they had dreamed of in a future daughter-in-law. She wondered if they would try to stop the wedding from happening. Georgie started to make whining sounds that usually announced a major tantrum. She tested the milk, pouring a few drops against the inside of her wrist. It was still too hot.

'Are you okay in there, Katie?' Tom's voice seemed a million miles away. 'We're all having seconds in here. Dad's been saying he hasn't had chowder this good since I was a baby.'

'Bet he hasn't,' Katie muttered to herself before stifling a groan at her joke. She saw the phone lying on the counter and put it in the pocket of her dress before going back into the dining room.

'Sweetheart, you're quite the cook!' Anne smiled, and Katie saw the spark of something that might one day turn into acceptance in her eyes. Her stomach rolled over. She'd ruined everything. Katie managed to mumble a thank you before taking Georgie into her arms and indicating with the bottle that she was going to feed him and put him to bed.

'Babe, I can do that, you've barely eaten!' Tom started to get up from his chair.

'No, no, you stay there.' Katie's face hurt from trying to smile. 'I'll be right back.'

Once safely upstairs in the nursery, Katie propped Georgie up with the bottle while dialling Jerry's number.

'What d'you do?' He didn't even ask who it was. His voice was a bit slower, his fifth whiskey, maybe his sixth.

'I used Georgie's milk, my *milk*.' Katie looked around to make sure no one had followed her upstairs. '*In the soup*,' she hissed.

'Oh, honey.' Jerry's voice sharpened from whiskey six to whiskey one in a heartbeat.

'What do I do?'

'Have they started to eat?'

'They're on their second helpings.'

'I suppose that's a compliment.'

'Don't be disgusting.'

'Seeing as you just fed your in-law's your own breast milk, honey, I don't think you're in a position to call anyone disgusting.' She heard Jerry pour himself another drink on the end of the line.

Katie blinked away tears. Georgie's eyes were rolling into the back of his head as he continued to suck away at the bottle.

'What am I going to do? I think they were starting to like me. And now, *this...*'

'There's nothing you can do. You don't have Hepatitis, do you?'

'I don't think so.'

'Then you're fine. I was reading this article about a guy who had to have a liver transplant because a wet nurse gave him Hepatitis C when he was a baby.'

Georgie's eyes opened as Katie stopped rocking, her hands shaking.

'Am I fine, Jerry? Am I fine? Or did I just make a soup that potentially gave my in-laws Hepatitis C?' she hissed frantically.

'Who knows? Maybe the virus goes away while you're cooking, like alcohol.'

'Very funny.'

'Just go back down there, be your beautiful, intelligent, dazzling self, and never speak of it ever again.'

'I might die of shame.'

'No, you won't. If you could, you would've died that Saturday night at Mehanata in February '06.'

'Don't remind me.'

Jerry sighed and Katie could hear his attention span waning. His voice had returned to a soft, slow whiskey two. 'What's done is done. It's like they say: no sense crying over breast milk.'

'Too soon.'

'Call me tomorrow. Go back to the party and forget about the whole thing. And bring Georgie to see his *daddy* soon.'

Katie hung up the phone and put Georgie down in his crib. Watery blue eyes stared up at her. He kicked his legs as if he was jumping horizontally and smiled. Katie stroked his velvety cheek.

Wiping her eyes, she took a deep breath and closed the nursery door behind her. Katie stopped to look at her reflection in the mirror at the top of the stairs and wiped mascara from her cheek. She fanned her face to dry her eyelashes. Her eyes weren't too red. It was okay.

It was silent downstairs. Katie wondered if they had gone to the sitting room. Tom had told her he had wanted to show them his new books on microplastics. *What a nerd.* Katie smiled.

If someone had told her a year ago that she would have been engaged to a man like that, well, maybe she wouldn't have convinced Jerry to go with her to the IVF clinic in Westchester two days after her thirty-second birthday. *What a horrible thing to say. What kind of mother are you, thinking like that.* She shook her head as if to erase the thoughts like they were unwanted lines in an Etch-a-Sketch. It was okay. *See, you didn't screw it up. Well, as far as they know, at any rate...*

Slowly, Katie made her way back down to the dining room. She thought of the Gifford's ice cream in the freezer. *Might be good with some maple syrup...*

'I'm back.' Katie entered the room, a genuine smile on her face.

No one moved. The Thompsons sat, frozen, in front of empty bowls of soup. Katie saw the pink tinge had left Anne Thompson's cheeks, and Greg looked slightly green. She turned to Tom. His eyes were focused on something in the distance, avoiding her gaze.

'Anyone ready for dessert?' Katie asked.

But as the words left her mouth, Georgie's cries filled the room. Nausea creeping back up her throat, Katie looked around for where the sound had come from. And then she saw it, its red light shining through Tom's fingers, knuckles gone white: the baby monitor.

Katsuki

Eva Pollet Lopez

The dream begins the same way each night.

He and Eiji are on the playground at the elementary school. Katsuki hasn't set foot there in years, but the memory is lifelike, right down to the rubber matting that scraped his knees raw when he fell and the shiny patches of silver in the jungle gym where the blue lacquer had rubbed off after years and years of wear.

Katsuki was only nine. It was the year Eiji broke his wrist and let him sign his name on his glow-in-the-dark cast with a blue permanent marker. He and Eiji laughed for weeks when the cast was taken off and his left forearm was thinner and weaker than his right.

He remembers because Eiji's arm had looked pitifully small the day he threw a punch at Taro's nose.

Taro started it. Katsuki had grown an inch or two the summer before fifth grade, but he could never outgrow the ugly, gnawing discomfort of being the gawky new kid with too-shiny shoes, planted in front of the classroom to introduce himself with a wavering voice.

When Taro approached, sneering down at Katsuki where he sat on the playground next to Eiji trading monster cards, Katsuki ignored him. Eiji ignored him too – until Taro swung a heavy leg at the pile of cards stacked between them. The cards went flying, scattering in every direction, and Taro's untied shoe hit Katsuki directly in the face.

Katsuki's hands flew to his mouth. His nose stung. His eyes watered and his vision blurred at the corners and something hot and violent burned beneath his skin at the unfocused sight of Taro's sneaker sitting in the space between his crossed legs. Blood pooled between his fingers, dripping from his cupped palms, and he watched one fat drop slip between his knuckles and *plop!* round and fat on the back of a card, where it left a rust-coloured smudge he could never quite rub out with his thumb.

In his dream, he lunges at Taro. His fists leave streaks of blood that mix with his own, and the bruises on Taro's face are mottled black and blue. In his dream, he doesn't live through the shame of wiping his bloodied hands on his pants and picking up the cards one by one without saying a word, swallowing the taste of blood and mucus past the lump in his throat.

In his dream, he doesn't resign himself to the unspoken knowledge that his father would deliver something much worse than Taro's humiliation if he returned home with a warning for fighting.

Nevermind that when Taro boxed in his face at the end of the school year and Katsuki choked on the molar he knocked loose, his father spat in his face and called him a coward. Katsuki flicked his tongue over the hole in his gums and chanted, *coward, coward, coward.* Cowardice tasted like missing teeth.

The final summer before the start of high school, the class took a field trip to the local art museum. Katsuki hates this part of the dream the most.

He was eleven and sweaty and uncomfortable, and his knees constantly ached. He sat on the bus seat with his knees drawn to his chest, head tucked in the space in between, motion sickness churning in his stomach. The sun burned hot through the rattling windowpane and all he could think was that his shirt clung to his back and the nape of his neck was damp and *Eiji wasn't there.*

The still air beside him was unfamiliar. It was years before Eiji made a habit of sitting with the popular kids; long before he became a popular kid and a star baseball player and Katsuki learned to lurk in his shadow with his head down, hands jammed into his pockets, shoulders jutting up towards ears that grew faster than the rest of him. Eiji's absence was strange then – it's not so strange now, when Katsuki eats lunch alone and takes the train home alone and sits in his room alone after school, *alone alone alone* – and the short ride to the local art museum was nothing like they had planned together.

Alone on the bus seat, Katsuki thought of Eiji. He imagined him tucked into bed, playing video games by himself and scheming new monster card strategies, and learned that abandonment tasted the same as rejection tasted the same as envy.

His feet dragged on the shiny museum floors. He had snuck away from the chaperones and crowds of students early on, and wandered through the galleries alone. Art made of glass, art made of paint, art made of trash, art made of nothing. (Empty space, he would learn later on. Not *nothing*. Just empty space.)

It reminded him of the kindergarten art projects he shoved into the bottom of his backpack and threw out in the bins behind the house without ever showing his father. Art was like the grass that used to grow on the lawn in front of his house. His father had mowed it all down and replaced it with concrete. *Gardens are impractical, boy,* he'd said in a voice no better than gravel. *A waste of money and a waste of time.*

Katsuki's bored pacing came to a stop in front of a sculpture, tucked inside an alcove.

He stared, unseeing, deciphering a tangled heap of steel until he made out the image of two men intertwined. *TWO CHERRY TREES, STILL IN BLOOM.* The words on the shiny placard did not make any sense. Katsuki stared at the place where the men were connected. He read the placard over and over, palms sweating, unable to explain why it made him feel sick, why it made him feel nervous, why he had the same feeling in his stomach that he did the time he and Eiji scarfed down ice cream sandwiches and then threw up in the marigold bushes behind Eiji's house after racing their bikes.

He couldn't tear his eyes away. He didn't hear the sound of the teacher calling his name and tuned out the footsteps of twenty fifth-graders heading in his direction. He was alone with the sculpture, dizzy with adrenaline, until the hall erupted with the cacophony of an entire class rioting, laughing, jeering. Katsuki's attention was violently ripped from the sculpture.

'Two old men!'

'Sick!'

'Katsuki's a *pervert!*'

Katsuki flinched at the sound of his own name. He balled his hands into fists and shoved them into his pockets and glared at his teacher for silencing them with an air of embarrassment. *This is a museum!* she scolded. *It's a quiet place where they use quiet voices!*

She said nothing about the sculpture.

Katsuki braved a glance over his shoulder as they walked towards the exits, returning to the bus that would take them back to the elementary school with the chipped-paint playground and hallways that smelled like urine. The sculpture was burned into his vision. The farther he walked, the smaller it looked, and buried beneath the hot shame and discomfort he couldn't explain, something inside him ached, rubbed raw and sore, like the inside of his cheek, gnawed between his teeth.

He stumbled over his own feet and saw the bodies touching, intertwined, behind the dots in his vision.

On the bus, he couldn't ignore the snickers and whispers. Boys moaned in high voices. Pairs of friends feigned grinding and humping one another, hands mocking, jeering, touching faces and caressing before shoving one another off, shouting, *gay!*

Katsuki sat alone in the front row, head tucked between his shoulders. His palms were slick with sweat and grew damp, no matter how many times he wiped them on the legs of his pants. He was burning from the inside out.

Eiji had stayed home sick, he thought uneasily. Maybe he had caught whatever Eiji had. Thinking about Eiji only made him feel worse. When the bus came to a stop in front of a railroad crossing, he threw up into the center aisle.

The dream changes again. But this time, the dream is different.

Katsuki sees himself. He's no longer prepubescent, and neither is Eiji. He stands in front of Katsuki as he is now, athletic and tall and broad in the shoulders. Cleats dangle from his gym bag and there's a dark patch of sweat in the center of his back, between the broad planes of his scapulae. He pinches the front of his shirt and pulls it away from his chest, fanning his torso, and Katsuki catches a glimpse of his tight abdomen and the waistband of his boxers peeking over the stretchy elastic band of his tiny exercise shorts.

Katsuki turns to himself again and sees his look of disgust, and he *remembers* this now, and fear grows in the pit of his stomach. He doesn't want to see this. Eiji laughs and pulls him into a tight embrace goodbye.

Katsuki can remember feeling the hard planes of his stomach underneath his sweat-translucent shirt. Katsuki knew then, just as he knows now, that he had held on longer than appropriate. Two years later and he still remembers how it felt when he couldn't bring himself to just let go.

They part ways and Katsuki follows himself. He watches himself walk stiffly down the endless stretch of street between Eiji's house and his own. He remembers the chafe of his inseam and the heat in his face, the astute shame that he's never been so aroused in his life as he was in that moment, holding on to Eiji.

Katsuki closes his eyes. He doesn't want to see himself. He doesn't need to keep his eyes open to know that he loosens the tight zipper of his pants as he walks up the steps to his bedroom, where he sags against the door and locks it behind himself.

Katsuki wakes up just before his hand reaches into his pants. He wakes up hot, covered in his own sweat and tangled in bedsheets he angrily kicks off. His cock pulses hard in his briefs and he grits his jaw, looking up at the ceiling and focusing on the poster taped above his bed, counting the number of seconds it takes before he can move without hissing. He refuses to touch himself, lying in bed ramrod-straight until it passes.

Another dream. They're getting worse every night. He wants to blame Eiji for all of it.

If Eiji hadn't reached a hand out to him in kindergarten, if Eiji hadn't punched Taro for him, if Eiji hadn't casually invited him to hang out at the arcade a week ago, as if the last two years of static silence meant nothing, *if, if, if*—

Katsuki runs a hand over his face, sighing heavily, and lies listless in bed, listening to the sound of blood rushing in his ears and his own harsh, uneven breathing.

He can't remember the faces of the sculpture at the museum. It happened so long ago, and yet the memory haunts him, no longer suppressed in the furthest corners of his subconscious. It's as embedded in him as the physical memory of that phantom tooth. He runs his tongue over the flat of his molar out of habit. It had long since grown in, but he remembers the sensation of his tongue finding that hollow and probing into his gums over and over, working at the empty space like a fixation.

He raises a hand to his mouth and touches his fingers to the stem of his lips, rubbing his thumb against his lower lip until it parts, and traces his front teeth with his index finger. The surface is smooth and flat, the edges and points of his teeth sharp and uneven. He closes his eyes and presses two fingers into his mouth, skimming the inside of his lips and the sensitive spot behind his lower teeth, and drums the tips of his fingers against his palate, shuddering violently when the sensation itches and makes him rub his tongue against the roof of his mouth over and over, until the sensitivity is near-unbearable.

When he touches his tongue, slippery and foreign between between his fingers, a moan slips through involuntarily. He presses two fingers down on the muscle, thinks *the hypoglossal nerve*, and curls his tongue around his fingers, pushing them deeper, licking the taste of salt from his own skin. All he can hear is the awful, slick squelch of his tongue sliding between his fingers and the wet gag when he *sucks* and his tongue pulses tight around his fingers.

Drool dribbles down his knuckles. He can feel it on his chin and on the palm of his hand, streaking the inside of his wrist. His fingertips graze the pocket of his cheek and the skin there is soft, so silky and smooth, he marvels over it until he recalls the gesture that flirtatious teenage girls make in the hallways at school, holding a fist to their cheek and popping their tongue into the socket. He thinks of Eiji.

What the hell are you doing? He can't get his fingers out of his mouth fast enough. The question rings in his head, over and over, and he tries to ignore just how much the voice in his skull sounds like Eiji's.

Repulsed, he wipes his wet fingers on the leg of his pajama pants – and freezes when he realizes that he's erect again. His stomach twists.

'Fuckin' freak,' he mutters under his breath, grounded by the sound of his own voice. He stares at the distended crotch of his pants, lip curled, and anger rises to displace the tension coiled in his stomach. His mouth tastes sour.

He's overwhelmingly aware of every sensation on his skin; the brush of his own hair at his temples, the bedding still caught around his ankles, his clothing and the friction on his skin. His fingers curl on his edge of his pillow.

Katsuki flicks the roof of his mouth and shudders. He'll never do that again.

Slowly, his pulse returns to normal, but the malaise lingers. The taste of bile is heavy on the back of his tongue and he fears that if he closes his eyes, he'll remember the feeling of his fingers in his mouth and the unnamed heat in his stomach when Eiji held him close and Katsuki breathed in the scent of sweat and cologne, boyish, still on the cusp of manhood. Eiji had never felt so close or so far as he did then, in Katsuki's arms.

He's grounded by the sound of his alarm. It's eight thirty in the morning. Saturday. Katsuki stands and opens the window, looking out into the cool spring morning. He hangs his head over the sill, breathing in deep and slow, and pushes all remaining thoughts of missing molars and art museums to the back of his mind.

When he raises his head, he sees Eiji at a distance. He's a blip at the end of the lane, dressed in a tank top and exercise shorts. A navy gym bag hangs over his shoulder. Katsuki cups his face in his hands and stares.

The feeling gnawing at his stomach is hunger, he decides. Nothing more, and nothing less.

But when Eiji turns at the end of the lane and waves unexpectedly, Katsuki freezes, and though Eiji is too far away to see, Katsuki smiles when he waves, before he closes the window and turns to his bed. His fingers skim the exposed stretch of his stomach between t-shirt and waistband, and as he settles back into his sheets, fingers already probing at his gums, the thought eats away at him, inescapable-unremitting-unforgiving – *oh no, it's something more.*

Grounds for Coffee

Harry Clough

We embraced for the first time in full view of the world,
Perfume thick under my nose,
trembling hands slipping inside
His coat to clutch themselves for warmth.
Our chins met briefly.
We walked, first side by side,
Then together.

We'd noticed each other for weeks,
Quick glances across the choir stalls.
When we locked eyes, a quick smile
Then back to the music
While my own song hummed inside.

He turned into the café and I followed, dazed
At our audacity to bare ourselves, for we were
Judged nakedly. The smell of ground coffee
Sank into my pores as we sat opposite each other;
Coats on the backs of our chairs,
cutting off the protection
We'd built around ourselves and talked about

Ourselves, each other, nonsense.
I watched his mouth, transfixed by his
Soft, tender voice, his eyes sparkled under
Christmas lighting, red, golden, and green.
Drinks forgotten, the world around us blurred
As we focused- in furtively, on each other.

Alien

Jack O'Rawe

When I was six and my brother was five, our parents called us into the living room to tell us they were getting a divorce. They asked us if we had any questions. I didn't. My brother asked what would happen to his goldfish. Nothing, my father said. Then he got in his car and drove off and my mother went upstairs and turned off all the lights and went to sleep.

Many years later, I stood in my garden in the snow and smoked a cigarette. The cigarette was bad and the garden was cold. I was out there because I had seen a ghost.

'It only has to be better,' said Ed. 'It only has to be better than last week and I think we're ok.'

His voice was small on the other end of the phone, flat and tin-sounding. I raised it back up to my ear.

'Better than what?' I asked.

'Better than last week. Better than last week and the boat remains un-rocked. Better than last week and it's a non-event. We like non-events.'

'We like non-events,' I said back. I must have said it without conviction because he took it as a question.

'Yes, we do,' he said. 'Because no one gets angry at non-events. Getting angry at non-events is like getting angry at nothing.'

'Do you believe in ghosts, Ed?' I asked.

'You're not listening to me,' he said. 'You're not listening.'

I glanced around the garden. Darkness welled in two black pockets in the far corners, but probably not enough for someone to hide in. Even someone small.

'I am,' I said. 'Non-events.'

The job was standard enough. Helene needed to end up in outer space, needed to slum it in a tin can the far side of Mars, and it was my job to get her there. The nature of the rewrite had turned out to be more extensive than advertised. Some scenes needed to be erased and replaced. Most just needed to be erased. It was that kind of a job. The original writer no longer existed. There was no name on the script when they sent it to me.

'We'll take it slow tonight, how about?' said Ed. 'Stay the course. Maybe go for the training academy stuff. Flight school. Cheryl said a lot about that on the phone. They want more meat there. They're thinking maybe there's space for something to go in there.'

'There isn't,' I said. 'I think it's a montage. I think it's *I Will Survive*. I think it's *The Air That I Breathe*.'

'I'm just telling you what Cheryl said,' said Ed. 'And I think for now we should stick to what Cheryl said. Until we find our feet again.'

I had been working on it for a few weeks now. It was garbage, naturally. It would still be garbage after a few rewrites too, but of a slightly more acceptable variety. Ed said I could use his holiday house. For the quiet, he said. At nights I sat in his office, at his desk, deforming myself over my keyboard. I jabbed at the keys with precision and ferocity, twisting and mangling the different letters, warping them all in and out of each other, expanding and contracting them into various combinations. During the day I slept in his bed.

He had a big portrait of his family hung over his desk. His wife and his kids. Swim trunks and bikinis and the sun and the sand. I guess he kept it there to remind him what he was doing it all for. It didn't remind me of anything.

'It's a montage,' I said. 'And then we save space for the bicycle stuff. For her with her daughter and the learning the bicycle.'

'They don't want that,' said Ed. 'That's not part of it.'

'It's the emotional core of the film.'

'It's not. They don't want it. It doesn't fit.'

'If I don't do the bicycle and the daughter, then it has no impact when she comes back home at the end.'

'Stop trying to bring her back,' said Ed. 'It ends with her in space. They don't like it when you try to bring her back.'

They did not want her to come back.

'Okay,' I said. 'Yeah, okay, whatever.'

The week before I had sent them eighty-two pages, fifty-seven of which, it turned out, had not been part of the outline they had included, had apparently just been invented by me. I was as surprised as anyone.

'Something slow tonight,' said Ed. 'Something simple. Until we find our feet.'

'Slow and simple,' I said. I glanced around the garden again, at the fat, lumpy white that had scabbed over the grass and the concrete. It wasn't snowing outside, but it had snowed. I hadn't seen it happen but it had happened. 'Slow and simple wins the race.'

'You're not listening,' said Ed. 'Are you listening?'

I looked down at the cigarette in my hand.

'Do I smoke?' I asked him.

'What?'

'Do I smoke?' I asked again. 'Do I smoke cigarettes?'

I couldn't remember if I smoked or not. It didn't look right in my hand.

'The fuck do you—? Of course you smoke. Or, I dunno, maybe you don't. What does it matter?'

'Yeah,' I said. 'I guess.'

'Are you sleeping?' asked Ed. 'Do you sleep?'

'I'm hanging up now,' I said.

I hung up.

The wind whistled languidly, came down cool from the sky and in through the scales of my skin. I hadn't really seen a ghost. I knew that. It was a trick of the light or something. An overactive imagination. I had come out to take a look just the same, though.

What it had looked like was a boy. A little small Victorian boy with neat brown hair and a tiny pale blue sailor suit. Brass buttons on the front and a thin white ribbon around the neck, standing dead-centre of the garden and looking up at the house with his small empty face. You could tell he was a ghost because he was pale. The fact I could picture the scene with such vivid clarity, in such detail and stillness, despite only glimpsing it for a fraction of a second through the upstairs bedroom window, told me that I almost definitely hadn't really seen anything. The image was somewhere in my head rather than my garden. Needless to say, when I came out to look, it was not there anymore. The garden was empty and there was no ghost. I stayed standing there, though.

I slid my phone back into my pocket and shivered a little. I'd have called my brother but the phone was new and the only number on it was Ed. There was also a number for someone named Hayley but it was missing two digits. We hadn't spoken in a while, me and my brother. No bad blood or anything. He just travelled a lot for work, moved between cities and time zones. He could be anywhere right now.

I wondered where I was, what city. It was dark here and there was snow. If I thought about it for long enough I would remember, but I didn't think and so I didn't remember.

A child, I had thought.

A child on the snow.

More than that, though. Worse than that. No eyes. Black holes for eyes. And a mouth wide open in a silent scream.

My fence coughed.

'Isaac,' I said. 'That you, buddy?'

'It is,' came his voice, disembodied, from the other side of the fence between our gardens. 'Just came out for a smoke. You good, Rick?'

'Yeah,' I said. I took a breath. 'I'm good.'

The fence was too high for us to see over it, to see each other, but we'd sometimes stand out here and talk. In fact, I hadn't actually seen him in the flesh in coming on a couple weeks. I was starting to forget what he looked like. I remembered he was old, though, but you could get that from the voice.

'You didn't see anything just now, did you?' I asked. 'Anything in my garden?'

'I can't see anything in your garden,' he said. I heard him take a puff and a second or two later I saw the smoke rise against the night air. 'On account of the fence.'

'Yeah,' I said. 'Never mind. Hey, Isaac, do you believe in ghosts?'

'Hm,' I heard him say. 'No. No, I don't think so.'

'I see,' I said. 'Fair enough.'

'I was struck by lightning once though.'

'You what?'

'I was struck by lightning once. When I was a boy.'

'Oh,' I said. 'What's the, uh, what's the connection to ghosts there?'

'I dunno,' he said. 'Weird.'

I went back inside.

The night my father left, my brother and I sat in the living room and watched television. It was the room with the fish tank in it and my brother sat next to it with the side of his head pressed against the glass and his hand hanging over the top, the tips of his fingers resting gently on the surface of the water. The fish was orange and yellow and it touched silently against my brother's fingers with its moon-shaped mouth. It had no name.

When my brother fell asleep I went into my mother's room. It was pitch dark and I sat on the edge of her bed and looked down at my hands in the shadows.

'Who's that?' she asked. She asked it without raising her head or moving her body.

'It's me,' I said.

'Oh,' she said. 'Hello.'

'Hi.'

I stopped looking at my hands, looked at the wall in front of me instead. It was black.

'I'll sit here for a bit if that's okay,' I had said.

'Yes,' she said. 'That's fine.'

I stayed up and worked all night. In the morning I sent Ed the pages and made myself an egg. He called me back a few hours later.

'None of this,' he said. 'Literally none of this.'

'Ok,' I said.

I deleted the draft and started again.

Re-Visioned

Margaret Abigail Flowers

We are wrapped in each other as dawn breaks, nestled together among sumptuous furs on the porch swing as the last snow of the season slowly melts into the soaked grass. You say you think the flower buds will be out in a week or two, winter wiped away without a trace. Tracing the soft lines of your waist, your back, I imagine those flowers blooming from beneath this unmarked expanse. You run your leg up mine, tease about how I haven't shaved in a few days, but you haven't either. I curl my hands around your hips, lean into your neck and breathe deep. The scent of you is springtime, incoming rainstorms, freshly cut grass. I have a feeling you're happiest in spring and summer, out in the sun where your hair will turn from dishwater blonde to radiant gold.

You sizzle with the approach of winter's end. It's a tingle on the tips of your fingers and toes that warms you from the outside in. You are anticipation personified, your movements quickening as if you were cold-blooded or returning from the land of the dead.

I've been comfortable in the cold forever, you've only now begun to adjust.

I don't say that I wish winter would continue, that we could stay enveloped here forever, feeding each other rich pomegranate seeds and remaining motionless for hours. There's a gentleness about the winter, the snow dampening all sound and rhythm until all that's left is us, together, breathing. The faintest sound of doe hooves on snow, the soft noise of crushed, icy velvet beyond the trees, is as soothing to me as the birdsong is to you.

This winter's love made all the sound we needed, kept us from feeling deaf in the dampness of it all. We broke off from the world for a while and spent time discovering every inch of skin; the inner crook of your elbow, the faint stretch marks on my breasts and abdomen, the way we fit so well together, your back to my front, your hands clutching my arms into your chest. Between the two of us, we'd crafted our own world. Seclusion, to me, is where reality begins.

But the snow is melting, the sun finally peeking out from behind a grey blanket of clouds, and, for the first time, you shiver beneath me from the chill. I can't help but realise the meter of us is changing, speeding up, becoming unstable. You're jittering beneath me, and I don't quite know how to keep you still.

Like some internal alarm has started clanging within you, you swiftly slip out from under me. As you return inside, you smile over your bare shoulder and it dazzles me, shocks me into awareness just as I'm left alone. The utter lack of you brings goosebumps to my skin, a starved ache to my gut, gnawing and writhing like a three-headed beast within. I gasp at the wrenching I feel but still tear myself from the rocking swing, following you into the once-warmed heat of the house, the fire now burned down to embers.

Your phone is your hand for the first time in what feels like ages, vibrating frantically as you switch it on. *My mother*, you say, *can't stand to be ignored.* Voicemails and missed calls and hundreds of messages. You read silently, then start to collect your clothing from the floor, pulling it on piece by piece and leaving me feeling suddenly unnatural in our once-beloved nakedness. You mention something about how she's not feeling well, and maybe you should go stay with her, just for a while, probably the spring if not the summer. I notice you don't say anything about me.

Does your mother know that I exist? Does she know how her golden girl has spent the frozen months – feasting between my thighs, relishing in the delicacy of darkness? If she did, she'd probably assume I was the one who had stolen you, locked you away in this cavernous hole of a home for all of winter to try and turn you against her, into some queen of the night. I've never been so ambitious.

I hold back from trying to make you stay, promises of venturing out into the world as the warmth returns stuck in my throat. You aren't one to stay in one place for long, and I'm not one to leave my den. Still, you promise to come back, murmur you'd be lost in the winter without me and that sweet fruit I give.

I say your name like a sigh – *Persy, Persy, Persy*. You don't like your full name, it's much too formal for one like you, and you like the pursing of my lips as I call you, like soft kisses blown into the air. I almost ask you not to go. You pull me in, run your fingertips up my neck, into my hair to massage my scalp in a way that makes me shiver. *Soon enough*, you say, as if you've pulled the plea from my mind.

I do not say that I will miss you, Persephone. I have no desire to hear your half-hearted response, because we both know I'm the one fallen here, the one trapped. Your mother might think I have stolen you, but she is wrong, for I'm the one who has been ripped apart by the wake of you as you resume a natural diet of sunlight and warmth.

You part with one last kiss, soft, a reminder that maybe you'll return when the land freezes over again and we'll be ladies of the winter together. When you're gone, I'm left to return to my cave, our once-haven, empty again, and though the sun is beginning to warm what little is left of the ice, the house remains cold and dark.

Sleeping Hermaphroditus
[*In the Louvre*]

Daniel Dicks

If I could say it out loud, I would
Tell you how I dreamed
Of anything else,
Anywhere else,
Of finding some way of shifting,
Of scattering myself
Living ashes not held,
Not bound in this place
Or to this marble-soft body.

How you weren't there,
Nobody was. Nobody
Watching me, running their eyes
Obsessively, along my thigh, along
The softest parts of my body,
And how that felt, to be unseen,
To be a secret carried in the wind,
To push my way through leaves and meadows
To know the smell and feel of loam
And shiver at the kiss of pearlescent sea-foam.

Personal Ad

Annie Diao

The first time I met Dan, I should have known he was special. Sure, dressed in an ill-fitted, worn-out t-shirt and black slacks, he didn't look like much. But those glazed brown eyes told a different story. Unkempt facial hair buried the shape of his jawline and when his yellow-brick teeth snagged the end of a cigarette, I thought of Australian bushfires. Had he ever accidentally set his own face alight?

Leaning against the red brick wall in the darkest corner of the alley, I waited for him to slip past me like all the others. For a second, his fingers played skittishly with a lighter; then, he noticed me.

'*Hello*, beautiful!' He sauntered across broken glass and cigarette butts. Halfway across the alley, his mud-flecked shoes came to an abrupt stop. His eyes flickered up and down the length of me. Something like wonder lit up his face. 'What's a pretty thing like you doing in a place like this?'

Five metres away, a stray dog lifted its hind leg and piss squirted into the crevices of the bricks. Pretty soon it would start to reek, and there was no way of knowing what else was waiting for me. It had been a long day. It would be an even longer night if I didn't try.

'Please, I was—' Kicked out? Abandoned? No longer wanted? No matter how many synonyms I tried, I couldn't finish that sentence. I didn't know how to. For days, I had watched people pass by me, some with eyes averted and others scrutinizing me with perverted curiosity. They all shared one trait: none of them would answer my cries for help. But Dan was special. He had noticed me. He had answered my pleading call.

Tilting his head, he asked, 'What can I do for you?'

I moved in. Dan carried me over the threshold and all the way into the corner of his one-room flat he called his 'bedroom'. His place was tiny – a dark, squalid ten square metres. Upon my insistence, he installed long, frilly curtains that divided the room into a kitchen, an actual bedroom, and a dining area. He replaced old bulbs with LED ones and repainted the cracked, mouldy walls. He even bought tiny bonsais to line against the freshly scrubbed window.

In the following months, we did all the simple, yet beautiful things lovers do - dinner dates and movie nights, whispers of future plans under the duvet. Our conversations would go on until the moon waned into morning light. We'd fight too, words hurtling like knives. But we'd eventually make up, followed by hours of sweaty, headboard-creaking activities. Between the grinding of his hips and his heavy moans, he would whisper how soft and perfect I felt beneath him.

So where did it all go wrong?

Did it start when Dan decided to tell his friends about us? Maybe it was before that. Dan was special and kind; if he could hear my cries for help, he could hear others' pleas, too. He *wanted* to help. Caught up in his own heroic fantasy, he started bringing them home. He carried them through *our* threshold.

Then, no matter how quiet or subtle they tried to be, the amorous sounds of heavy panting and hoarse whispers still punctuated through the curtains.

'I didn't mean to,' Dan would sob after it was over, after he had tossed them out of his door as proof that it would never happen again. 'I don't love them. I love *you*.'

I didn't say those words back. I let the brooding silence fill the spaces where conversations should have been. Late into the night, my mind often drifted to the two people who had loved me into existence, but no longer loved each other. In mutual agreement, they had packed their bags and sold their house. Neither of them had wanted me. I had been too much of a witness – a reminder of the failure of their marriage.

Dan started coming home late. He slept on the couch and cried into the phone. I pretended not to hear him. I pretended not to hear his friends either. But more often than not, I'd fall asleep hearing their voices telling Dan that he was out of his mind for dating me. Their words - *'This is so wrong, Dan. It's not normal to feel this way'* and *'you need help'* became a haunting mantra but no matter how many times his friends emphasized that he should start counselling sessions, they never once mentioned anything about couples therapy.

Then Dan started seeing *her*. Monica.

The day he showed up in the apartment breathless and flushed, I should have known to expect the worst. But still, when the words tripped out of his mouth, I couldn't believe it. Eying all the movable fixtures lined up neatly by the doorway, ready for transportation, I asked, 'We're leaving the country?'

Dan's neck flushed crimson. He stopped pacing in the bedroom. 'It's just me,' he exhaled. 'Not we. *I'm* leaving.'

Silence.

I scrambled and unscrambled his words. I could hear the velvet armchairs and the French drawers mocking me from their lineup. A rare clarity gripped me. 'So you're taking everything else with you. Everything but me.'

Dan scratched his head, sheepish. 'You… wouldn't fit.'

Wouldn't fit into his future plans or wouldn't fit into his van?

'Are you calling me *fat*?' All those nights we'd spent together, all those nights he'd spent on top of me, as he reached one climax after another. 'You said I was the best thing that ever happened to you!'

Dan swallowed. 'I'm sorry. I—'

His apology only fuelled my anger and a torrent of accusations creaked out of me. 'You have an actual bedroom, discovered shaving, and dressed properly. It's all because of me! People only started liking you once they could see your chin! Why would you do this to me?'

'I'm sorry, I'm sorry.' His hand stretched forward but, at the last minute, he stopped himself.

Understanding flashed through me. 'It's her, isn't it?'

He averted his gaze. But it was enough.

'But I'm the one who carried you through the darkest nights. Don't you remember all those times when you cried yourself to sleep on top of me?'

Dan laced his fingers into his disheveled hair. A low whimper escaped him. 'I do, I do…' His narrow shoulders shook, then stilled. 'But it isn't right for anyone to be dating a mattress and you *are* just a mattress…'

I wanted to howl, to deny that claim. I was funny and witty and an amazing listener. But the limbless, rectangleness of me faltered. I was only all those things because Dan was special. Because *he* could hear me. For a split second, I wished I could borrow Dan's hands – veiny and strong – so the slap across his face would smart. So he could feel the hurt torsioning through me, springing and compressing against the metal coils of my heart.

Feebly, I reminded him, 'You said I brought light into your life.'

'You did.' Dan nodded. 'I would've never gotten those LED bulbs or scrubbed my window if it weren't for you. My flat would still be a craphole.' Squaring his jaw, he continued, 'But Monica said I have attachment issues. This will be for the best.'

I had lost the battle before I could even assemble my army. 'So, what will happen to me?'

He stroked my sides. For a split second, I envisioned being made out of memory foam so my skin could remember the shape of his fingertips. I ached to be held but his arms never made it that far. 'You're a custom-made piece of art, baby,' said Dan earnestly. 'And when I found you in the alley, you were almost brand new. I'm sure you're still wanted.'

But I wasn't brand new anymore. I was ruined. Stained by coffee, sex, and puddles of saliva. Even in my soiled condition, however, I would have liked to think that I could still muster a shred of dignity. So I said to him, 'Dan, call up Monica. Tell your psychologist the truth. Tell her about your obsession with the wash basin and how you cheated on me with that dumb dining table. Tell her about the filthy appliances you found in the dumpster and how you'd fuck them, toss them, and crawl back to me. Tell her about our relationship, too. Tell her the whole truth.'

Dan's eyes widened. 'Wh-why?'

'Because you've just been breaking up with your mattress. You clearly need more help than you think.'

After that, I embraced the role of being nothing more than a mattress. No matter how much he swore, cried, and screamed, I remained silent.

The day before Dan moved away, he hauled me to the front yard. At my request, he stuck a sign beside me:

'Single mattress looking for love.'

Mint Cigarettes

Samira Safarzadeh

Her left foot stepped on the leathery skin of the chair as her right foot found its way to the table under the window, pressed against the wall. She hoisted herself up, then sat down, bringing her legs closer to her chest as if to make herself smaller for this big world. Her slender fingers pulled out the pack of mint-flavoured cigarettes from her pocket. She lazily opened the cap and picked one out. Her other hand found the handle of the window, twisting it open, letting the chilly fall air hit her skin. She welcomed the cold as if it was a dear friend.

She gently wrapped her lips around the cigarette and brought the lighter close to her face. She flicked the wheel and stared at the fire, letting it flame until her skin burned. But her eyes were fixed on the flickering blue, orange, and yellow in utter fascination, like a child seeing flame for the first time, and not knowing what to do with them. So, she set her cigarette alight, relieving her thumb from the flame and her heart from the pain, watching the tiny grey wisps simmer in the air.

She took a drag, closing her eyes in pleasure like one would when breathing the fresh air of the mountains. The smoke slowly rolled down her throat to her lungs, soothing her every muscle, her every sinew like a lover's touch. She held the smoke in until her lungs begged for air, and when she started seeing black dots in the corner of her eyes, she finally let herself breathe once more.

She looked at the moon as if she was having a silent conversation with it, and when she was done, she flashed her middle finger to the skies. Whatever the moon and the skies told her was only between them. Not that it mattered. Today, all that mattered was sitting on top of her table and indifferently smoking her mint-flavoured cigarettes, the rest of life a distant afterthought.

The saying goes 'Once in a blue moon.' This was one of those nights. The moon was blue, as was she. Blue all over, fusing with her red blood into a regal purple. The pack of mint cigarettes was teasing her from across the table, but this night was different. She didn't want to smoke her worries away. She sat on her table, like so many other nights, remembering a line from a poem she once wrote: *how many times does a heart break before there is nothing left to break.* Well, she knew the answer now. Once was enough.

She knew life was unfair. On this blue moon, she came to understand how unfair love could be. She had lots of men loving her without conditions, loving her even though she did not love them back. Loving, hoping, and wishing that maybe one day her gaze would shift to them. But her eyes always seemed to find the undeserving ones in the crowd. The ones that liked the convenience, the ones that liked to play. Perhaps it was the familiarity of the toxicity that pulled her to them, addicted to the sweet poison just like with her cigarettes. The good, the unfamiliar – those scared her away.

She was always the type of person to say, 'Here is all my affection, take it.' But she never said it to the right people. The right people just loved her without reciprocation. She wondered if fairness, like true love, was real. She wondered if she would ever experience them both.

She had gotten her heart broken once on a rainy day in October. It was as ugly as it could get. Both the Eiffel Tower and he refused to break their silence as she walked away, spine artificially straight, her sobs genuine.

After a year, she was ready to try again. So she found another man to love, gave him all the tools so he could love her right. She said, 'Baby do not play me, and I will make the stars align for us.'

But he looked at her in confusion and said, 'The stars move too fast and too far, by the time we see them align, our time will already be in the past.'

So in late October, this new man tried to break her heart, but instead of a loud crashing of waves, you could only hear the soft ripples of a receding tide. On this particular fall blue moon, she hugged her legs close to her body, their familiar place, and wished to feel the beating of her heart against her chest once again. Just to know it could be rebuilt, even if it currently lay in pieces.

She looked at her cigarettes and gave in. She lit one and let the smoke take over her frizzled thoughts, pushing the pain away till it was nothing but white noise. With each inhale the memories of this familiar, yet unfamiliar man grew sharper.

After their first date, she made a pit stop to buy cigarettes before meeting up with her friend at the bar. Later she held her spritz and cigarette with her right hand, the left being too occupied with enthusiastic gestures as she told her friend everything whilst the Parisian wind played with her hair. She rarely smoked, only when in

Paris, only when too drunk to care, only when she was scared. So, she smoked then.

They were in the Louvre. He was looking at the art and she glanced at him from the corner of her eyes and thought everything was perfect – almost like the serenity one gets from the first drag. It was strange to think that just in two months' time she thought of him as a dear friend, as a person whom her soul deeply resonated with even though they had nearly nothing in common. But even if they were fundamentally different people, something just clicked. Something beyond her comprehension. It was terrifying. But between the arms around her waist and the kisses on her neck, she found it hard to think about anything else.

November rolled around; goodbyes were said. She knew it would eventually happen. Deep down, she had always known. But she never wanted to admit it.

Maybe she was still in denial, or maybe she had long accepted this truth, nestled in between parted lips and the spaces between their bodies when the dark thoughts slowly crept in. She was sure with him she would learn to feel again. Now she would never find out what was waiting for her beyond the edge. She put her cigarette in the ashtray and took her phone from the table. With clumsy fingers, she clicked on the video from their first date. She picked out her cigarette and pressed play. This time, she let the tears find their way to her mouth, mingling salt with smoke.

She was sitting on the cold pavement by the Seine, the one under the Alexander Bridge. There was something that pulled a person in when they looked at her, something that whispered, 'Come find my secrets,' that all the passers-by noticed. The bulky man exercising behind her couldn't keep his eyes from her exposed nape. She was well aware, and she reveled in it. The man couldn't place where he knew her from exactly, and only at the end of his workout would he remember her crying face, the one he'd seen at the library all those months ago. He had never found out why she was crying, just as he would never ever find out why she shed a tear by the Seine.

She closed her eyes and turned to the sun like a flower basking in its warmth. She could feel the man's gaze. So she smiled an empty smile, a flower dropped and stepped on before it could bloom. She wondered how many times her heart would have to break until, instead of tattered fragments, all that was left was dust. But she never seemed to break, at least not fully, not with an audience. You just found her petals scattered, decaying throughout the earth.

In her grey coat, she sat down by the Seine as a tear broke free from its confines. She blamed it on the sun. No one believed her, not even herself. Not even the Seine. All she wanted was to be somebody's something. To belong. But she only ever belonged to her mint cigarettes.

When the sun set behind the Seine, she picked the lone cigarette from the otherwise empty pack. One final cigarette.

Souvenir du Soir

Daniel Dicks

Like an old film, degraded and hazy,
The river, grey water against grey bricks,
Moves slowly, perhaps not at all.
The water, looking always to the sky,
Changes with it, like a lover,
Now to black and white.
I thought I saw the stars there
But I suppose it was only the street lamps
Rippling their light across the surface
(orange or yellow or white?),
Scattering long shadows
Along the banks and bridges.
So now I remember your silhouette
Walking just ahead, turning to look back.
Now, your smell, your warmth,
Your awkwardness,
Your face, which revealed everything,
Every thought written there in some language
I wish I'd taken the time to learn.
Perhaps I said something funny,
Though I don't remember what,
Only your smile,

So wide your eyes would close to fit it...

Forget that now, though.
It hurts too much, remembering.

Who's A Clever Boy? Mummy Loves You.

Josephine Balfour–Oatts

Are you planning on going back to work soon? they ask. A concerned smile, head tipped to one side. I tell them the truth: that I'm too busy picking packets of Crayola up off the floor. I can't, I say. Too bogged down, playing Noughts & Crosses, I say. He always wins; with his every go he gets three in a row! Who's a clever boy?

He's even better at Hangman, I tell them. Laughs like his father when my stick figures get caught in the noose. He draws houses, too. That's a picture of the apple tree outside. That's a sketch of next door's dog. This one's painted in the past tense. That's a still life of something that hasn't been invented yet. And I think that's supposed to be me... brilliant, isn't he?

D A Y T I M E
I S
P L A Y T I M E

Have you thought about getting some help? they ask. A concerned smile, head tipped to one side. I tell them the whole truth:

that we are managing perfectly fine on our own. He's just learned to spell his name. Today, I say, I found a curling cursive crawling across the floorboards, the windows, the bathroom mirror. I found large letters made of tea bags and coffee grounds, knives and forks, ballpoint pens. Who's a clever boy?

I don't need to hire a babysitter; I don't need to hire a nanny. Besides, I continue, pointing to the writing on the wall:

B A T H   T I M E

I S

B O N D I N G

T I M E

In the water, my bonny boy sings. He squeezes a sponge that looks like a strawberry; the suds smell like spring. His favourite colour is green. I know because he told me. Who's a clever boy? The magic stops when he starts to scream; bath time becomes bedtime and he's converting milk into mayhem and it won't stop it won't stop it won't—

Stop, listen to this: if I knock on the door of my stomach, the emptiness echoes like a tantrum and nobody answers because nobody's home.

N I G H _ _ I M E

I S

_ A _ _   _ I M E

In the dark, minutes tick, taking longer than hours. I cover my eyes with my eye mask, with my hands, with gravel from the back garden, with the tie that Mark left behind. There is the taste of tap water on my tongue. The duvet makes fists around my fingers. In the shadows I spy a walking mouth; the stars staring through the window; the spaces between songs on a CD; the feeling of a secret; a sudden sound in the shape of a memory.

Would you like to hold him? they asked. A concerned smile, head tipped to one side. I told them the whole truth and nothing but the truth: that I couldn't even carry him for nine months. Their smile turned sad; the silence was bigger than the baby. He didn't scream, then. Not even when they pressed his skin to my skin. Not even when I prised his little lids open, or when I tried to coax the breath from his body. Mummy loves you, I said. He was soft and still and silent. But most of all, he was *my* favourite colour. Blue.

The Abyss Calls

Morgan Waas

Every town is known for something – a landmark, a local quirk, a particularly gruesome crime. For Sasal, it is the Abyss. The bottomless chasm looms at the edge of town, the darkness lapping at its borders.

Rina had seen the shadows move.

Long ago, one of Sasal's leaders decided to capitalise on the presence of the Abyss, renaming buildings and constructing attractions to add to the "atmosphere" of the place. Some of the changes stuck, including the name of the inn where Rina worked – the Edge of the World.

It was a stupid name. Rina had always thought so. The Abyss was not very wide, and the world continued on the other side. There was even a bridge across it. But for all she groaned internally each time she thought about the name, she had a good job there. Samis, the owner, was kind and paid her well. Her own father had disappeared when she was a child, and in some ways Samis filled the void he left behind.

Summer had been an unusually quiet season in recent years. The locals still stopped in for food or drinks, but the rooms upstairs were largely vacant. There was one guest staying there now – a merchant in town for the upcoming Midsummer Festival – but he had shown himself to be on the reclusive side, and had retreated to his room when a group of local men arrived to get a head start on the festivities. Now that they were gone and Samis was in his kitchen office, Rina was alone in the common room. She thought she could hear the merchant talking upstairs but could not be sure.

The inn was boring when it was slow. Rina could only clean so much before she felt like she was losing her mind. Adding to her discomfort, the room was stifling despite the open windows, which seemed to only let in snippets of speech so faint she could rarely make them out.

She wished one of the Watchers would visit. The men and women who guarded the Edge of the Abyss often stopped in after their shifts and were always good for an interesting story. So far, though, they were absent. She had not heard from Samis in a while, though that was hardly unusual. Since the death of his wife, he had started retreating more often to his office, leaving Rina to gradually take over most of the day-to-day operations. She had even hired the new cook.

Finally, after an age, the midnight bell released Rina from her work. She left the common room for the kitchen.

'I'm fixin' t'leave, Samis!'

No answer.

She knocked on his office door. When there was still no answer, she pushed it open.

'I said I'm leavin', sir.'

She glanced into the office. Samis sat limp in his chair while a large grey creature gnawed on his shoulder. It was similar in form to a panther, but, where a cat would have fur, there was only mottled grey skin and pale, pupil-less eyes. From its grip on his flesh, it seemed almost ready to drag him away. When the deepfang spotted her, it placed a protective paw on Samis's chest, pushing him down, and hissed, blood dripping from its teeth.

'Not again,' Rina rolled her eyes.

She turned and ran out of the building, hoisting her skirt up to free her legs. On the corner was a warning bell mounted on a post. There were dozens like it in town, especially near the Edge. The pealing of the bell cut through the quiet night, followed by the clanking of the Watchers' armoured footsteps. One stopped next to her while his fellows continued inside. She knew what he was going to ask and answered before he did.

'There's a deepfang. Right in through the kitchen, chewin' on Samis.'

'How long's it been there?'

'I dunno.'

The Watcher nodded at her.

'Thanks, miss, we'll take it from here. You head on home, quick-like.'

'Yessir.'

The Watchers' work was secret, though everyone had their suspicions. Rina tried not to think about it. When she returned to the inn, the creature would be gone and Samis would have no recollection of the event. It had unnerved her the first time, but it was such a regular occurrence now that she just put it out of her mind as she walked home.

Rina hated summer. Even at night, the heat was oppressive. She had already tied her hair up in a futile attempt to cool off, but beads of sweat still trickled down the nape of her neck and the centre of her back.

She was almost home when somebody spoke her name. It was just a whisper, soft enough that she almost missed it, but undoubtedly someone was calling to her.

'Hello?' Rina glanced around. Nobody. The voice came again, from a direction she could not place, and this time she could not understand its words.

Sasal was safe enough, aside from the occasional intrusions from the Abyss, but this felt wrong. With an added urgency to her steps, she hurried home.

When she finally crawled into bed, she found herself unable to sleep despite her exhaustion. Every time she started to drift off, the memory of that voice returned to haunt her. Part of her wished that she had been able to make out what it was saying, but another part was glad that she could not. Though at first it had seemed sinister, as she turned it over in her head, replaying the way it sounded, Rina realised that there was a kindness about it. It knew something that would help her. She almost wanted to hear it again. Just to know what it had to say.

Rina woke in a tangle of sheets, having wrestled with them throughout a restless night. She dressed and prepared for another long, slow day at the inn before joining the crowd that swarmed the streets. She wove her way through the market, shading her eyes from the sun. Snippets of gossip met her as she went.

'Y'all hear the bells go off last night?'

'Yeah, down by the inn? Wonder what happened.'

'You'd think Samis would be more careful about that kind of thing, being so close to the Edge, and after last time—'

'He just doesn't care anymore. I worry about everyone who works there.'

Rina ignored the voices around her and continued to make her way toward the inn.

Every child in Sasal is told stories about the Abyss. Some were about how the Abyss lured people into it, never to be seen again. Others were about how it twisted your thoughts, changing you forever. When Rina was a child, no one alive could remember the Abyss being that powerful.

The supernatural presence of the Abyss had faded into myth. Many believed that whatever lurked in the depths had died. Some questioned whether it ever existed in the first place. Elders warned that the Abyss was simply dormant, waiting for the right time to return. But it was hard to instil fear of an absent enemy. The Abyss creatures retreated, the movements of the darkness slowed, the sounds that rose from its depths quieted.

At least, until three years ago.

It was Rina's second year working at the inn. She was friends with Samis's wife, Anna, a kind woman who was always laughing. Because they were so close, Rina noticed when she started to change. Anna became more distant. She talked to herself, and gazed out the window at the Abyss for hours.

On Midsummer, Rina and Anna, acting like herself again, had gone to the market in anticipation of a busy night. Rina carried the baskets on their way back, and had waited at the door for Anna to open it. When she did not, Rina had looked to see Anna walking across the open ground between the inn and the Edge. She had called out, but Anna just kept walking. Rina ran after her friend, screaming for the Watchers as Anna got closer. She grabbed Anna's arm and dug her heels into the dirt, scraping divots into the earth as Anna pulled her with an unnatural strength.

Anna stopped at the Edge. Rina remembered laughing in relief. Then Anna looked at her, smiled, and took another step. Rina, still holding her arm, had nearly been pulled in with her. A Watcher pulled her to safety as Anna disappeared into the darkness.

Everyone became more afraid after that. They added new locks and painted ritual symbols on their doors. The Watchers doubled their ranks and built walls along the Edge. The old stories were told once again. Tourists stopped visiting Sasal. The Abyss was no longer an oddity but a threat. Strange sounds filtered from its depths. Whispers drifted through the air. Deepfangs ventured out to torment the villagers, slipping through the cracks. The darkness began to rise and fall like the tides.

Samis was the only one who did not take extra precautions, despite the advice and insults from others. Rina privately thought that he was intentionally making himself an easy target.

When she got to the inn, Samis was at the bar. He looked just as he always did, with no signs of the attack except for a sliver of bandage peeking out from under his shirt collar.

'Mornin' Samis. You all right?'

He jumped slightly when she spoke. 'Hey, Rina. You doin' well this morning?'

'Yeah, I'm all right. It's hot as anythin' out there.' She smiled at him and put her things behind the counter, ignoring that he had ducked her question.

'Midsummer's always hot.'

'I didn't even realize it was Midsummer!' She unconsciously flinched at the forgotten anniversary.

'Look, Rina,' Samis placed a hand on Rina's shoulder. His voice shook as he spoke. 'I wanna say thank you. For everything. I know you tried to save Anna, and you've been saving me ever since. I'm leavin' this place to you, someday. I know you can handle it. You do most of the work already.'

Before Rina could respond, Samis chuckled and disappeared into the kitchen. She shook off the strange feeling of discomfort and started the process of opening the inn – wiping down the bar, opening the windows, and setting the tables. A voice – was it the same one that spoke to her last night? – crept into the corners of her mind. It was clearer, closer now. It reminded her of someone. Anna, maybe, or was it her father?

Come and see, it said. Come and see your friends. Your family. Everyone awaits you here. Forget the light that holds you back.

Rina focused on her tasks, trying to keep her thoughts clear. She was beginning to regret her late-night wish to hear it again.

When the merchant came downstairs an hour later, she passed his breakfast order back to Samis in the kitchen as the cook was not in yet. She was relieved to see Samis. After his declaration, she had half-expected to find him dead.

The guest left for the day and no one else came in. She expected a slow morning and a busy night with the Midsummer celebrations.

The voice continued whispering, echoing her errant hopes or wishes, offering her anything she had ever wanted.

You can be free of your worries about your friends, safe from the pain of loss. Come and see what awaits you here. Give us a chance.

It left an oily, cold sensation in her mind and numbed her body. She felt her gaze drawn to the window against her will. Her fingers froze and she dropped the glass she was holding. The sound broke her trance, chasing the voice away.

Samis appeared with a knife in his hand.

'What's happenin'?' He saw Rina kneeling amidst the shards of glass and came over to help. 'Why're you breakin' my things?'

'I'm sorry. I don't know what happened. I must've dropped it. I—' she paused, unsure. Her head was pounding. She felt disoriented. 'I don't remember.'

Samis frowned and swept up a pile of glass.

'I don't like the sound of that. I'm gonna go get one of the Watchers. You stay right here, you hear?'

'Yessir.'

Rina did not know where the nearest Watcher was, but hopefully Samis would be back soon, with help.

She frowned. Why was she at the front door? She had no memory of leaving the bar. She had agreed to stay inside. She was outside now, turning to go back. The voice was louder now. It could answer questions, all the questions she ever wanted to ask. It felt pushy now, demanding that she come speak with it. If she did, she would accept its offer.

Her feet moved without her command. Her mind was fuzzy.

She walked towards the bridge.

In the distance, she could hear footsteps, getting closer. She walked faster.

The planks shifted under her weight. It was almost beautiful from up here. She could look down forever. What secrets lived in the dark? A shadow trailed up from the Abyss, reaching towards her. She could discover them. Rina reached out to it.

A cacophony of voices cheered her on. They were unintelligible now, all speaking over each other in their excitement.

'Dammit, girl!' Samis grabbed her from behind, wrapping both arms around her to hold her in place. She stumbled.

Let her come. One voice spoke independently while the rest shrieked their anger. Let her come back to me.

The bridge swayed on its tethers. Rina fought his grasp and stood. Why would he not leave her alone? She reached for the shadow again.

'Y'all gonna help?' He was not talking to her. 'Or are y'all gonna let her go too?'

A single voice rose out of the chorus, calling for both of them. Samis's grip on Rina tightened as he heard it too. A soft sob forced its way from his throat as he recognised it.

More hands grabbed her, pinning her to the bridge. Samis stood in front of her. He kissed her cheek and turned to face the chasm.

'Listen here! I'll make you a deal!' He glanced back briefly. 'You can have me, if you leave these people alone. So long as I can see my wife.'

The Abyss accepted. The tendril of shadow wrapped around Samis's waist as Rina went limp in the Watchers' grasp, its hold over her broken. Anna sang her delight.

'Samis, no! It's a trick!'

It was too late. Samis smiled back at her as he fell into the dark.

Every town is known for someone – a great leader, a philanthropist, a hero. Sasal remembers Samis, not for his sacrifice but for its futility.

For a while, the people know peace.

But the creatures return. Sasal takes up arms against the darkness. The cycle of the Abyss begins anew.

Rina never does rename the inn.

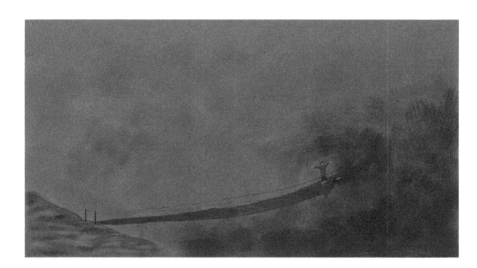

The Photocopy Archivist

Alex Marceau

Cool, November morning. The sun sits on top of Mont-Rigaud.
7:51 a.m.

Last night I worked late into the evening and did not join my son
to watch the hockey game, so I am thumbing through *The Suburban*
at my desk, collecting analytic fodder for small talk at lunch. The
grainy photograph on the front page reveals Théodore slouched over
his goalie stick with the puck in the net behind him. After thirty-four
minutes of ice-time, he let in five goals from twelve shots, a mere
0.42 saving percentage. The Montreal Canadiens have lost yet again,
despite winning twenty-four Stanley Cups.

I loosen my necktie and scoff at the framed photograph on my
desk. 5'9" and 193 lbs. On the ice, I was unstoppable – even I could
have scored against *Théo*. But of course, like most men, I stopped
lacing my skates years ago in exchange for work where, now, I simply
aim to complete these lunchtime post-game reports before Pascal
arrives.
7:52 a.m.

Employees leak into the building and their footsteps reverberate throughout the stairwell. Unlike most people at the office, who walk around the building greeting others before settling down at their desks, Pascal is forced to acknowledge his primary work station immediately upon arrival. The flights of stairs bring him face-to-face with the Xerox 914 and my desk, which faces this peculiar photocopy machine.

This morning it hums listlessly.

7:53 a.m.

When I started working at *Kitsilano Ltd.* as the Content Creator – or, as my colleagues prefer, the Tool – a marketing intern told me that an extra minute in bed in the morning was a sin: 'Yes, yes … every man's shoes oughta be shined, but Molson watches you through the glass from his office there in the corner – not from up there,' he said, glancing towards the blank panelled-ceiling. 'Should you stay in the nest too long, you won't roll under the Sainte-Anne-de-Bellevue overpass by 7:54 a.m., where the next minute, the local train rolls by to block our way.'

The intern's devotion reminded me of my grandmother, who'd fall asleep with her pink rosary. He liked being the first to arrive at the office because flicking the lights on in an empty building is the only control a working man has: 'I don't flick the light-switch at dawn for the sun to come up, you know.'

The intern was predictable.

Pascal is not.

There are mornings when he's not escalating the stairs alone and I can decipher his *cluck cluck* from the *click clack* of Lousanne's high heels; or, if he is alone racing up the stairs, he might open the door wild-eyed and sweating, as if a fire erupted and Hades was making photocopies of his ass. Yet, on those fine mornings after a Habs victory, Pascal is calm. The rising *cluck cluck* sounds like hockey sticks battling for a loose puck, and at the top of the stairs, I can hear him humming the tune of CBC's *Hockey Night in Canada*.

Whatever it may be today, I am lucky, for the report is complete and his unexpected entrance will not deter my concentration.

So I wait.

7:55 a.m.

It is time to use the washroom.

June 10, 1993. My first day with *Kitsilano Ltd.*

The humidity enveloped everything it touched, sucking whatever water was left from my pores. Trees stood lazily on the side of the service road and I had a light headache. On my wrist, tucked beneath my shirt cuff, the red stamp from La Cage Aux Sports.

The CFO's brother, Gerard Kitsilano, greeted me outside the front door of the office building and, soon after, began kicking a pebble. Over the past seven years, it has become painfully obvious that if it were not for his brother Molson, this corpulent man would not be here. He greeted the new employees, showed them around the building to their desks, and then waited until someone else was hired to repeat the tasks. Gerard occupied a unique position in the HR department, but we all pitied him.

So it was: 8:00 a.m. and still, no sign of Pascal, the other new hiree. Gerard had the newspaper tucked in his back pocket and I could read part of the headline, 'ADIENS WIN STA'.

'Did you watch the game last night?' I asked.

'Mighty great game that was,' he said. 'I was just reading all about it before you got here.'

'Another Stanley Cup and Conn Smythe Trophy with the Habs for *Saint Patrick* Roy! He's quite the goalie, eh?'

Gerard kicked and followed the pebble until it fell off the curb. He scuffed his heel and sighed. 'Yes, well, I wonder if Pascal is going to show up or if his skinny limbs are still hanging over the railing at the Forum,' he said. 'We've got a busy day. The fall catalogue is due in six weeks.'

He picked up the pebble, placed it back before him on the sidewalk, and resumed his idle kicking game. 'Say, do you know much about hand tools?' he asked.

I stepped into the shade. The words seemed to batter my temples.

'I've used them before, yeah.'

'Well, I hope you enjoy tool specifications. You'll be quite the expert.'

Before I could answer him, a man walked toward us from the service road, slightly limping. The air was getting thicker, a city bus peeled away, and against the pale sky, he looked like a hunched banana beneath the weight of a bag slung over his shoulder. He was clad in brown corduroy trousers, a red polo shirt, and loafers. A thudding *cluck cluck* pummeled my temples. There were no construction workers in sight and Gerard had stopped kicking his pebble. *Cluck cluck.* The nearer the man got, the louder the sound.

'Hi, I'm Pascal. Sorry I'm late, Gerard,' he said, panting. 'Did you guys watch the game last night?'

'The game can wait, okay? Let's get inside. Have you used a Xerox 914 before?'

'Yes, yes, of course. Good game though, wasn't it? Another Cup!'

'Please, Pascal. Now, so long as you keep Molson's photocopy machine printing, people will keep filling their toolboxes with our tools.'

We went inside and the thud returned, *cluck cluck*, every second step.

The next hour slipped into an amorphous ball of 'you knows' and 'yeah, well, you'll get the hang of it.' Gerard seemed to know as much as we did about his brother's company: 'So this is the marketing team, they do ... you know ... they get our products into people's *psyches*,' he said to us, laughing alone. 'Behind them is the content team, they do ... well, I guess you know, since that's what you got hired for,' he said, pointing to me.

And on he went.

When we stopped in front of Pascal's desk, he carefully placed his bag down on the floor against the filing cabinet. Before fastening the zipper, as if to conceal something only he was privy to, I noticed a folder with the inscription, *Montreal Canadiens: Stanley Cup Final, June 9, 1993. Pascal Duchamps.*

I opened my mouth to say something but Gerard sighed evenly and said, 'Well Pascal, there are several reports in the cabinets for you to start classifying. Get to know them. Should you have any questions about the system, you can ask Molson tomorrow. Now, in the west wing you'll find extra supplies, and if any technical issues with the photocopy machine arise, well, that's why you're here!'

And just like that, we left him.

Gerard motioned me down the hall toward my desk, in front of the Xerox 914. 'Seems like Amanda left you last year's catalogues,' he said, gesturing toward the tomes stacked beside the computer.

'They're much bigger than I thought.'

'Well, you'll have plenty to keep busy.'

'What happened to her?'

'Ah! Well, she ... well, you know how it is these days. Some people just can't leave the workhorse at the stable for the evening.'

'I suppose.'

'Amanda, well, I don't know everything, but I do know that constantly recording specifications sort of ... well, you know ... it carried over to other aspects of her life. It seems that some people simply get tired of doing the same thing everyday and wind up needing a sick-leave.'

'Right,' I said.

'You'll be alright! Look at me, it's been five years, and I'm doing fine! Anyway, get to know the catalogues. If you have any questions, Molson will be in tomorrow.'

'Great.'

And just like that, Gerard made for the stairwell.

8 a.m. to 5 p.m., I remember thinking – *nothing before, nothing after.*
The man's heavy body tumbled down each step, until I was left alone
at my desk in front of the humming photocopy machine. Although
Gerard is an odd fellow, there are days when I wonder if on that first
morning, he had inadvertently warned me of how life unfolds for the
working man without any ice-time. Perhaps all we get are pebbles.

The sun is still hanging over Mont-Rigaud and people are now seated
at their desks.

7:58 a.m.

On my way out from the washroom, I walked around the whole
floor before arriving at the Xerox 914. Looking down at my desk
from this vantage point, I think of Pascal. For seven years he's tended
this machine like a gardener and his plants, and every morning, at
precisely 8:30 a.m., while he prints the previous day's financial report,
I catch a glimpse of him peeking around and smelling the sheets
before bringing them to Molson.

I can imagine them now: the technician and the CFO, standing
in front of a large painting that hangs behind Molson's desk. Kids
skate on a frozen lake in front of a small church and rolling white
hills. A familiar sight, that Canadian winter. Some of them wear blue
Toronto Maple Leafs sweaters and others the Habs' *tricolore* – blue,
white, and red.

When Pascal forgets to close the door behind him, I am lucky,
for I am privy to their analysis of the previous night's game.

'I'll tell you what,' Molson begins. 'Koivu is going to be one of
the best players to wear the *tricolore*. We might very well have to retire
his number and raise it in the building. The Lafleur and Carboneau
days are over; this is a faster game – the boys need more size, more
vision.'

'Two goals and two assists, eh? He played well, but on D you've
got Brisebois and Bergeron. The play starts from the back end, you
know.'

'It's not the defencemen who are filling the net with pucks,' Molson says. 'Duchy and Kitsy didn't score all *that* often.'

They both laugh.

If Molson still had the choice, I suspect that he would be a hockey analyst on *Hockey Night in Canada*. When the Canadiens lose, the players take a beating. I'd bet he believes he could put more pucks in the net or hit Sundin harder than any of those guys on the ice. But he's a numbers analyst, with that familiar painting of the idyllic sport hung behind his desk; a gentle reminder of our pastime that is melting away.

7:59 a.m.

Standing at the Xerox 914, I glance down at the recycling bin. There are a few photocopies of labelled photographs. I fetch a handful: 'Montreal Canadiens: Patrick Roy First Game, Feb. 23, 1985'; 'Montreal Canadiens: Stanley Cup Champions, June 9, 1993'; 'Montreal Canadiens: The Forum Closing Ceremony, March 11, 1996'; 'Montreal Canadiens: Vincent Damphousse (First Goal at the Molson Centre), March 16, 1996'.

I have witnessed these moments, either in one of these two rinks, or over the CBC's television broadcast.

There are more photographs, but Pascal's *cluck cluck* halts behind me. He must have slipped into the building while I was in the washroom.

'Good moments, eh? Did you watch the game last night?' he says.

'Yes, I ... well, no, I didn't. I read about it in *The Suburban* though.'

'Ah, the *Burban*, yes. Well, Théodore got pulled early, eh? He was like Swiss cheese with holes large enough to fit a beach ball!'

I chuckled. There are stains beneath his armpits and Pascal still wore that red polo shirt, though now, I notice the Canadiens' embroidered logo over his left breast – the C with the H in it.

'What are these?' I ask.

'Oh! Well, photocopies of photographs I've taken.'

'I recognize a few of these.'

'Is that so?'

The air conditioner by the stairwell spits a few times, and then all at once, blows cold air. I tighten my necktie.

'What are you doing with them?' I ask.

'Well, I've been appointed as Photocopy Archivist for a new project at the CBC Archives Centre. They think the internet will keep expanding, so they want me to compile a digital archive. A bit better than printing catalogues for tools, I'd say.'

'Have you been photographing the team for a while?'

'Say, you're quite curious, eh? A few years. My dad played for the Habs with Gerard's and Molson's brother, Félix.'

'Did you play?'

'Sure I did, until I got hit hard from behind. Big guy from Whitby. I fell into the boards awkwardly and broke my leg. Ever since then I've had hardware in here,' he says, pointing to his right leg.

'It seems we all stop playing at some point, eh?'

'Yep!' he says. 'But we're all drawn back to it in one way or another.'

'You're right on that one,' I say, glancing down at my desk. 'So, do you go to every home game then?'

'All of them!'

'Lucky you.'

'Some might say ... My old man passed in 1993, two weeks before the Habs beat the Kings in the Cup final. He had a heart attack—'

'That was *your* dad?'

'Yep ... he and Félix were the starting defence pair; Duchy and Kitsy. You know, I used to watch the games with Molson and Gerard at the Forum.'

'Like, *Molson* Molson?'

'Yep! That fella in the corner. He knew I liked to collect memorabilia, so when his new project of building the Molson Centre kicked off in '93, right after the win, he asked me if I wanted to document the construction and the games.'

'You mean the new rink?'

'Yep! An eye for history, eh? When Molson bought the Forum and the Canadiens moved to the Molson Centre, *Kitsilano Inc.* became his side project.'

'So you're outside the tool box, then. Lucky man.'

'Well, I think for Molson, having me here is like having Duchy and Kitsy back on *D*. We had fun, watching them. Now I capture everything my dad could no longer be a part of.'

I slowly flip through the rest of the bundle in my hands: Guy Lafleur, Larry Robinson, Bob Gainey, Mark Recchi, Chris Chelios, Guy Carbonneau, the Stanley Cup being hoisted at the Forum. These photographs capture the *tricolore*'s rise and fall from 1985 to 2000. As I looked at the more recent photos, I imagined my son watching the game. These were his stars, as I had mine. The weight of every photograph pressed into my hands, and the silence of the pending work day fell between us.

'Say, we both started here together the morning after the Habs won the Cup, eh? *That* was a good game,' he says.

'Yes, it was.'

'Those copies there aren't great, but keep them if you want.'

'I'll give them to my son, I suppose. Thanks.'

Pascal walks away to his desk, *cluck cluck*, and I look down at mine. It occurs to me that I have never checked to see who takes the photographs for *The Suburban*, and I wonder what else there is to know about all the lingering footsteps.

But the stairwell is quiet, for everyone is at work.

The photocopy machine hums.

8:03 a.m.

Third Quarter Moon

Daniela Castillo

As night fell in Barcelona, the clouds were painted onto the sky like brushstrokes, reflecting over the puddles on the street like works of art.

I was on my shift break and had gone to the alley behind the restaurant. It was so quiet I thought I could almost hear Barcelona whispering the dreams of its inhabitants.

I had quit smoking a few months earlier, though I still had the habit of going through the backdoor of Can Guillem and chewing on the tip of the ballpoint pen I always carried behind my ear to take orders. It was a far cry from a cigarette, but holding the cylindrical tube between my lips managed to conjure the ghost of my old

Ducados, if only for a few seconds. The ink droplets on the corner of my mouth evoked memories of a slight tobacco aftertaste.

My bun was messy, my apron had saffron stains around the edges, and my shoes were killing me – common indications that the night had been busy. As I leaned absentmindedly against the wall, I could hear the hands of my watch counting the end of my ten minutes of freedom. I balanced the pen between my teeth and leaned over to scatter the remains of a *bocata* among the stray cats that prowled around the restaurant. That was when I saw him.

It was his howl that gave him away. Otherwise, I wouldn't have spotted him. It seemed to me that he had always been there, hidden among the shadows in a camouflage made of a hand-me-down coat and ashes. I wasn't that surprised, though. Even if they didn't do it on purpose, almost every homeless person had that inherent ability to be invisible. Especially in the streets of Barcelona.

The homeless man was bent over himself. His whimpers were sorrowful and, from time to time, he looked up to the sky and shed some tears, which were lost among the street puddles. He seemed to be suffering from unbearable pain, but I could not immediately see any damage.

'It's gone... it's gone!' the man wailed.

Worried, I approached him, placing the ballpoint behind my ear again. 'Are you all right?' I asked. But, as much as I tried, I couldn't find the source of his pain.

'It's gone... poof...' His hands trembled uncontrollably and his weeping left two salt traces down his cheeks. I looked him over from head to toe, but saw no signs of damage on his run-down clothes. His wailing continued. 'It's not there! It's gone forever...'

'What's gone?' I asked, but when he didn't answer, I followed the direction of his gaze toward the kaleidoscope of clouds that painted the sky.

'The moon,' he whimpered at last. His black-stained finger pointed at the immensity of the celestial vault. You could barely see the slight glimmer of a star behind the upcoming storm. 'The moon is gone!'

'The moon is still there, sir,' my voice was slow and clear, but I made sure I had enough room to back off in case I needed it. After all, my *Yaya* had always told me that madness was contagious, that's how she had caught it many years ago, when she still remembered who she was.

'It's just cloudy.' I tried to get him to look up to the sky, but the old man squirmed like a little kid. A few drops of rain fell on his face and mixed with his tears.

'No,' he moaned. 'It's not there anymore... the moon is gone!'

'It's not!' I insisted. I was certain there wasn't a new moon that night and that the rainy season had just claimed the moon's custody for a few moments. 'The moon doesn't just... go. If you wait a little, you'll see it again.'

But the man didn't listen. He continued to shake his head over and over and pulled away from my touch as I tried to comfort him. His shoulders were shaking and his whimpers were growing more pitiful and disheartening by the minute. Rain began to fall incessantly and soon turned into a storm. I hesitated. As the end of my break approached, I realised his dementia had an expiry date for me. My boss would not appreciate me bringing a homeless man into the back storeroom, but I couldn't just leave someone so vulnerable to his own devices in the middle of a night like this.

'Come with me,' I said, in a final desperate attempt. Being very conscious not to hurt him or to further disturb the old man, I tried to guide him inside the restaurant and offer him shelter from the rain. 'I'll give you a glass of hot wine and you can wait by the fire until...'

I couldn't finish. The old man couldn't stop crying and his shrieks became so high-pitched and afflicted that they soon began to attract the neighbours' eyes, peeking out from behind their curtains.

'The moon! My moon! Where has it gone?!'

I desperately chewed the pen that dreamed of being a cigarette, without a clue of how to appease the overagitated stranger and avoid more indiscrete glances. And that's when it hit me. My *Yaya* also said that the most brilliant and stupidest ideas always come up at night.

In spite of his whimpers, I briskly took the old man's hand and with a shaky, uncertain stroke, I drew a third-quarter moon in the middle of his palm.

The illustration worked like a spell. The man stopped his cries and stared at the inked moon between his fingers, then he looked at me, incredulous. His eyes might have had an excess of tears, but they lacked years. Their awe was so palpable that it seemed to me as if he was discovering the world for the first time. Had I only seen those blue irises, I would have thought he was just a boy.

I tried to say something else, but I couldn't. The man closed his pocket moon in his fist and put it inside his jacket. Without another look, he limped away down the alley. I blinked and he was gone. I couldn't tell if he had turned around the corner or disappeared among the shadows.

Soaked, I held in a sigh and cleaned the smeared eyeliner that hung from my lower lids. God, how I wish I had a real cigarette. I bit the end of my ballpoint pen, but the placebo didn't work this time. It wasn't until I put it behind my ear again that I noticed my hands were shaking. I had gifted my time to the stranger, which meant that I had but seconds to pull myself together before crafting the fake smile I used to wait on tables.

The storm stopped and I prepared to get back to work. However, before opening the back door again and returning to the warmth of the kitchen, I dared to take one last look at the sky. There weren't any clouds or raindrops, not even the forensic evidence that proved there once was satellite up in the skies. The darkness was so deep that it almost swallowed my pupils.

The moon really was gone.

I went back to the restaurant and finished the rest of my shift, but as I picked up plates and cleared out food scraps, I wondered if the moon had really disappeared. Maybe the brush-like clouds had temporarily painted over it and played optical illusions on the both of us, or maybe the exhaustion and the lack of nicotine had made me imagine the odd vagrant in the back alley. Or even worse, maybe all the strange events of the evening did happen and I was an accomplice in the crime of the man who once stole the moon in the palm of his hand.

Wedding Days

Anna Koulouris

The veined marble floor of the cathedral stretches before her. Translucent stains of blue, red, and purple cast from high windows flicker beneath her feet. She scans the pews dotted with updos, auburn dye jobs, crew cuts, gleaming bald spots, and backs wrapped in sequins, florals, and suit jackets. Up ahead, seated in the middle pew on the left side, is the head she has slept with for half of her life. Next to his, a narrow head with shiny blonde hair turned out slightly at the ends skims his shoulder with each movement. A sliver of powdered cheek and a flash of eyelashes turn to him admiringly. Her breath catches at the scene. Even though she has prepared for it, the sight of someone else near him feels like a violation somewhere deep, as if to some untouched part of the soul. She realises she must sit before the music plays. Gravitating to where they used to sit takes the least amount of mental energy, so she takes long, quick steps to the right, resolving to take deep breaths until the sick feeling in her stomach subsides. The moment her thighs touch the pew, long notes spill from the organ and she rises.

The heavy doors with lapis beveled windows slowly swung out. She slid her arm through her grandfather's, throwing her gaze to the ceiling when she noticed his ninety-year-old eyes brimming with tears. With that burgundy runner, the aisle looked impossibly long. Down at the other end, he faced her head-on, not at an angle like the priest had suggested the night before. He had done that thing with his hair – combed it straight back the way it was when they first met. It was familiar – that vision of him in sharp black against white, hands folded down in front, widening the breadth of his chest and shoulders – in the way that an old photograph is familiar. The scene had unfolded so many times in her mind over the years that this may very well have been one more unfolding. But when the pipe organ bellowed, she was like an onlooker in a strange and wonderful dream. A colorful blur of faces flanked her, markers pointing the way, rows of poppies. Their eyes locked. With each of her steps his expression deepened, as if she were clicking through a slideshow of his heart's depth. He was crying. No, he wasn't. He was crying. But he always could control it so well. He was the one who had taught her to look up to keep the tears from tumbling down her cheeks. A stream of time flowed through them; waters that rose, churned, and fell. Glances and a shy hello. Him begging her to meet for wine. An antique bird pulled out of his jacket pocket. A tender kiss under a maple tree with a warm palm on her cheek. The porcelain bowl of spaghetti sauce spilling onto her satin blouse at his parents' house. Him nervously thumbing the rim of her linen skirt the first time he said I love you. And as she floated down the aisle to him, he watched, as if she were a vessel carrying his entire existence.

The organ blasts its finale. The groom clasps his new wife's hand tenderly and she returns the gesture triumphantly, waving her bouquet of lilies. Guests on each side of the aisle stand and face each other. He startles slightly when their eyes meet. She supposes that seeing her unexpectedly like this is a bit like catching one's own reflection in a mirror one had forgotten was there. The woman with blonde hair looks up toward the altar, eyes saturated with hope for the future. The shiny pale hair flashes around her neck each time she turns the powdered cheek and eyelashes up to meet his gaze, squinching her nose. The woman's black dress fits tightly around each curve, holding her breasts like cupped hands. His fingertips rest on the slope of the woman's waist. As soon as the newly married couple passes, apples of cheeks joyfully protruding, he and the woman with blonde hair turn out of their pew with at least one limb in constant contact with the other's lower back, upper arm, or nape of neck. As they exit, the woman clenches a fistful of rose petals from a wicker basket on the left, and he slips a cupped hand into the basket on the right, leaning down from his towering height to kiss the tiny flower girl on the temple. Stepping into shafts of sunlight pouring in from the cathedral's main entrance, they transform into silhouettes. The outline of their knotted hands diminishes as they pass through the brilliant square of doorway.

'Are you ready?' he asked, fluttering his eyes in the sunlight, smiling so hard that his lips got stuck on his drying teeth. 'I think so,' she giggled, shielding her brow with the white rose bouquet.
They stepped over the threshold of the wide doorway onto concrete steps, instantly shaded from blinding light by a cascade of deep red petals, which floated down softly onto her veil and tickled their cheeks and caught in his tuxedo lapels. The sole of his rented patent leather shoe slipped over the tulle of her dress and he tipped backward suddenly but caught himself and they fell forward together laughing and stumbling straight into the shiny vintage Cadillac – a surprise, ordered by his older brother, still stationed in Afghanistan.

Hundreds of name cards are lined neatly over the table plane like miniature white tents. She purposely lingers in the lobby while they're picked at to avoid being first in the room. But waitstaff at the newly opened reception hall are overly eager to help. She thanks the young girl who points her to the cards, spotting her name by its unmistakable length rather than by reading the thin cursive in the dim light. Table 8. Her table companions begin to hover around the No. 8 sign in its delicate metal stand like moths to a flame, bouncing from side to side before claiming a chair. An uncle of the bride whom she met at a birthday party twelve years ago is the only person she knows. She remembers his jovial disposition at that backyard picnic, urged on by several glasses of wine. But he is genuinely happy to see her in his presently sober state, as is she, and they make small talk over dinner until the quartet begins to play and the couple are announced over a loudspeaker. Like a veil of relief being drawn over her, the low lighting and crowdedness offer no view of him. There is too much and yet nothing to say. Across the sea of heads and creamy satin-draped chairs and bursting puffs of white hydrangea with bundled green stems stuffed into large flute glass vases, the groom lifts the bride's hand into the air and guides her into a delicate spin onto the dance floor.

The Cadillac crunched up the gravel path. He clicked open the door and ran around the back – it took four strides; she counted the dig of his shoes into the pebbles – to her side to unlatch the door for her. She leaned up to the rearview mirror to check her mascara. The breeze was sweet and cool around her; it felt like music. Looking up at him from the deep seat of the Cadillac, she saw an angel haloed with sunlight. With one hand he scooped up an armful of tulle. The other hand, in a mock-prince gesture, took her fingers and let her press on him like a lever to lift herself out of the car. The photographer hadn't found the place yet, but they were happy to be alone briefly. Everyone had said being married felt exactly the same, but she could have sworn it felt different, like jumping into the middle of the ocean and knowing you won't drown. They looked down the hill to the maple tree and then up at one another. 'Do you remember?' she asked. Glowing brown-and-amber irises bored into her soul. She couldn't believe how after all this time her stomach could drop. The corners of his mouth pressed into dimples. 'Of course I remember.' She screamed as he lifted her into both arms and carried her the rest of the way down the hill, tulle flying up blocking his sight.

It had been late October, five years earlier, when he took her there for the first time. He appeared on a Harley in front of her campus apartment at six. She had spent two hours dressing but ended up wearing the outfit she had tried on first, a mini-skirt and cherry red turtleneck. He hadn't mentioned the Harley. She was nervous and overcompensated by acting way too edgy, throwing the helmet on as if she wouldn't have accepted any other mode of transportation. As he whipped around the big, empty roads lined with spruces all she could concentrate on was keeping the bottle of cabernet they had picked up lodged between her bare legs. When they got to the park the view stretched for miles. Orange and red leaves burned like fire against a slate sky. They shared the bottle and talked until dusk. He leaned her against the maple tree and rough bark pressed into the back of her thighs. He put his hand against her cheek and for some reason she thought, this looks like a fireplace. *And that it had been a mistake to wear the miniskirt. Then he kissed her.*

Couples trickle onto the dance floor to join the bride and groom. The quartet is playing one of those love songs from a popular movie that no one can resist. The uncle asks her if she wants to dance. She doesn't, but then he pleads and makes her laugh so hard that refusing wouldn't make sense, so she leads the way, weaving through tables, up to the conjoined pairs. They sway awkwardly until their rhythms align. The lights dim further so that everything is cast in deep gold and the soft chinking of hundreds of plates fills the room as servers set down dessert and coffee cups. Each couple turns a degree with each sway, like moving cogs that circulate the newlyweds. As her eyes involuntarily lift from the parquet, it's her turn to be startled. Beyond the sturdy shoulder of her dancing partner are those amber irises. He is facing her less than a metre away, head framed by the bare shoulders and slim neck of the woman with blonde hair. His thumb gently pauses from circling the small of the woman's back. They can't turn away or their partners will notice the cut, so, for approximately one minute, he and she surrender into each other's eyes, saying without speaking, the thing that for three years has been left unsaid: are you happy now? *Is anyone happy?*

'I don't understand what you see in these.' She had forced him to come with her to the Degas exhibit the summer before they got engaged. He lost his temper after nearly three hours of ballerinas and naked old women getting into tubs. When she found him outside on the public bench reading a newspaper, it was clear she had been crying. He was devastated when she told him her father, who had always called her ballerina, had taken her to the Degas exhibit in Paris the month before he died. The next day he begged her to meet for breakfast. One of those monochromatic diners on the corner that make perfect coffee and towering stacks of pancakes. He pulled out a bag he had been keeping on the empty chair beside him and drew out a little enamel box – velvet inside with a spinning ballerina. When they got engaged that Christmas, she was too afraid to shower or wash dishes with the ring on. She kept it in the box most days. 'What good is a diamond closed in a box?' he'd say every so often. It came with them to their first apartment and every apartment after that. She still had it. She wondered if the music box still worked. And she regretted not keeping the ring on her finger in the shower when she had the chance.

The song draws softly to an end. The scene on the dance floor dissipates like smoke brushed away by a hand. A towering cake vined with rosebuds rolls out with a server guarding each corner. The groom is handed a large knife which he holds with two hands and the bride places her hand around his. They hold this position for a few moments, smiling while the photographer's flash captures them in white light and imprints the image into the vision of the guests until their momentary blindness subsides. The thin dish of cake rests in the bride's hands and the groom digs into it playfully with an elegant dessert fork. The bride pulls back coyly, as if warning him to feed it to her delicately. When it seems the groom has secured his wife's trust, she leans forward with her lips parted but he pulls the fork away. The guests chuckle collectively; a few let out whistles. After one more attempt at this game, the groom places the fork to the bride's lips and then bends down to her height so she can feed him a bite too. While cake is being distributed, the newlyweds circle the room to greet and thank everyone. As they approach Table 8, the bride reaches her arms out in advance of their embrace, shaking her hands excitedly like she used to do in her varsity dance competitions. They squeeze tightly and she pulls back to appraise and compliment the wedding dress, remembering how the girl used to play dress up when they'd visit her parents. She watches the couple eventually trail over to Table 22. He embraces the groom and they strongly pat each other's backs four times. The bride and the woman with blonde hair, much closer in age, dip down in laughter and wrap their arms around one another. Watching their bond from afar, she wonders whether spending years watching a little girl grow, giving her advice, and loving her, counts more. The newly married couple drifts past the array of tables into an abandoned doorway of the ballroom. Their silhouettes merge into one, lips touching, wedding dress and suit pants combining. Her elbow lifts and blends into the back of his neck. The room has thinned out. Table 22 is empty.

They found their room number in the hallway of the hotel. Husband, *she thought. They kissed in the doorway, framed by creamy walls with crown molding. His breath carried the champagne. She pulled back, fumbling into his pocket for the key card—'Let's get inside.' He let her use the bathroom first. The satin nightgown hung from the rod of the shower curtain as she washed her face and fingered through her hair for bobby pins. She slipped the nightgown over her head and noticed how her breasts lifted the satin. He was sitting on the edge of the bed but stood when she came out, clicking off the television. They stared silently at one another. His eyes appeared full, yet endless in their capacity to see her. Vessels carrying her existence now. Warmth settled in her lower belly like red wine and her limbs became heavy. He gathered her close and squeezed her to his chest. 'I love you forever,' he whispered.*

Ice Cream

Kate Lavelle

'It's a drug front, right?' Hallie asked from her perch on the fire escape ladder. Night had chilled the metal and she cooled her back against the wrought-iron railing. She was balancing her Lagunitas on her lap.

'What are you talking about?' Jacob asked, looking at Hallie over his shoulder. His brow furrowed, she could see the sweat glistening on his forehead.

'The ice cream trucks,' she said.

The boys were standing opposite her, drinking and looking down at the passersby heading to the bars up the street. From the fourth floor, the noise from the street was muffled but the laughter and shouts after friends carried. In the distance played a high-pitched nursery tune. Jacob side-eyed Andrew before he opened his mouth. 'I don't get it. Why would you think that?'

'I mean, no one is actually buying that ice cream,' she replied. 'They drive around Brooklyn at all hours of the day, playing that same goddamn song, never stopping, I've never seen anyone – well, okay one time, but – I've never really seen anyone buy anything from any of them. Ever.'

'How would you even know—' Andrew started to ask, but Hallie cut him off.

'It's, like,' she looked down at her watch. 'It's almost midnight and you seriously expect me to believe that these ice cream trucks are still doing business at nine forty-two on a Thursday night?' She sipped the beer in her hand and said, 'They're laundering money through it, I swear to god.' She finished it. 'And I hear that fucking music in my dreams.'

'But why— why the ice cream truck?' Andrew asked.

'I don't know, I just have a hard time believing that anyone could really run a viable business with that kind of model, you know?'

Andrew shrugged. 'I guess I've never really thought about it.'

'Okay, well you're thinking about it now,' she said pointedly.

'Dude, I work in public radio,' Andrew said. 'This is so not my forte.'

Hallie grinned but Jacob still looked skeptical. 'So you're saying, you think that the ice cream men, drivers, whatever, are drug dealers and they deal from their ice cream truck?'

'No, no.' She shook her head and took a moment to consider before attempting to break it down. 'The ice cream truck is a fake business. They launder money through the trucks.'

'And they actually sell ice cream?' Jacob asked.

'Well, yeah, of course,' she said.

Jacob tried to ask, 'So what's the—'

But Hallie ignored him and continued, 'Look, I'm just saying none of you, neither of you, can tell me that you actually see people buy ice cream from the ice cream trucks. They drive around all summer long and no one buys ice cream from them, how the fuck could they possibly afford gas, storage, parking. And they have to pay their drivers. Obviously, it's a cash-heavy business because, I don't know, they probably take card but, I don't think that that many people would necessarily need to pay card for an ice cream—'

'Wait, that's just absurd,' Andrew interrupted.

'Why?'

'This isn't an episode of Ozark,' he said.

'I know that. This is a conspiracy theory,' she explained matter-of-factly.

'A boring one,' said Jacob.

'Yeah, that's the point. The best money laundering schemes have to be too mundane to draw any attention, right? They're like New York's groundhogs, letting us know that winter is almost over. It's one of the main summer sounds, right; dripping window AC units, the twenty-four/seven spray of the playground sprinklers, and the ice cream truck song. They start driving around in, like, April when it's barely even warm out and then they drive around all summer long until October or whenever it's cold again and they're out there from like noon or earlier until nine p.m. or later, like, I swear to God, I've hear the ice cream truck way after dark, I hear it like at ten at night when I'm trying to sleep or not sleep or—'

'But why the ice cream truck?' Jacob asked.

'I don't know, I'm not a drug dealer.' Hallie pulled herself to standing and brushed the dirt off the back of her shorts.

'Well, not anymore,' Jacob smirked.

'Fuck off.'

'You know what they say: great minds think alike, et cetera, et cetera.' He laughed.

Hallie narrowed her eyes at him. 'Ritalin isn't a real drug,' she said. Then she crouched down and pulled up the window. She climbed back into the living room and stuck her head out behind her to say, 'I'm getting another drink, do you want anything?'

'Yeah, an ice cream cone,' Jacob said, still grinning.

Hallie held up her middle finger as she pulled the window down with her other hand.

It was the beginning of the previous winter and it was cold, though not frosty, but Myrtle wasis an aboveground station and the trains were only running every ten minutes on the weekends. They could hear the train squeaking around the corner as they walked up to Myrtle/Broadway and Jacob's first instinct was to start jogging. Hallie didn't run, she barely picked up her pace. They were almost a full block away from the intersection and the light wasn't even green.

"We're not going to make it!" she yelled after him.

He was wrapped up in his favorite coat and beanie but he could feel the cold pushing into the skin around his neck as he ran, like ice clawing into his skin. He could see his breath as he puffed and he knew there was no point, she wasn't going to try to make it and he would have to wait for her on the platform anyway, but still, he'd already started running and so he figured he shouldn't stop.

He wrenched open the doors to the station, dodged the alighting passengers, and just managed to swipe his metro card through the turnstile when he heard the three high-pitched notes that marked the starting of the train. He stopped jogging then.

She met him on the platform a minute or two later, not winded, not sweating, just smiling. He met her eyes and they walked on to be near the front of the train when the next car pulled in. The platform was empty, and the wind was more pressing at their new height. Hallie pulled out her phone to check the train times so they could text Andrew their ETA.

"Shit," she said, checking behind her to see if the display's estimation was the same as the number on her phone. It was; the next Forest Hills-bound M train was 14 minutes away.

"Well, tell Andrew we're going to be late because you missed the train," he said.

"Oh please, we wouldn't't've made it anyway." She started unbuttoning her coat. "Gives us more time to drink, though," she said with a knowing cock of her head. She pulled a Diet Coke and a flask out from inside the lining, then stuck the flask between her knees and the Coke under her armpit so she could do up her coat again.

"Here," Jacob said, grabbing the soda from under her arm. "What's in there?"

"I'm not sure, actually. Maybe tequila. I dunno, it's whatever was in there from last time."

"Nice," he scoffed.

"Thank you, I try." She freed the flask from between her knees and half-curtsied, before unscrewing the top, sniffing, and audibly gagging.

"Yikes." He pulled out two nips of José Cuervo, dangling the little bottles between his fingers like keys. "Should we start with these then?" He unscrewed the tops and handed her one.

"Cheers," she said, and they clinked their tiny bottles together before downing the whiskey: he in one sip, she in three. They tossed their evidence in the trash can and walked even further down the platform. Hallie was taking turns holding the Coke in each of her hands, alternately stuffing one in her coat pocket and then the other. Jacob craned his neck out over the cracks, but the only light was way far down the J track. He couldn't see anything around the M's bend.

They didn't look at each other very much. Somehow, though they were alone together in their apartment all the time, being alone together in public felt more intimate. He pulled his phone out of his pocket so he'd have somewhere to put his eyes. Reflexively, he started swiping on Hinge. She could see the little photos out of the corner of her eye, though the way his thumb was moving would've been give away enough.

"I thought you liked the guy from last night?" she asked him.

Not looking up, he answered, "I did. But it was just a first date and we haven't really talked yet today, so..." He shrugged.

She looked him up and down, considering. Then she said, "I don't understand how you do it."

"It's easy."

"But is it fun?"

"It can be," he said. "On the right night, with the right person even a date you know you'll never see again can be a good time."

She grimaced.

"You should try it," he continued.

"Yeah," she said. "Maybe."

She looked around the platform again, just to see who else was out on the first truly cold Friday of the year. She looked at their shoes as they each did the exact same thing: walked up the staircase, scanned the platform front to back before picking a side, walked along to find an available space in-between two metal pillars, craned their heads over the track to check for the train, and took a few steps back before pulling out their phones. Some particularly good boots made nice click-clacks as they passed; they made a sound Hallie thought seemed very grown-up and city "chic," though she knew they were just shoes. And not even as practical as her beat up Vans, though she needed to figure out what she was going to do when it finally snowed.

No longer entertained, Jacob slipped his phone back into his pocket. He stepped to the edge of the platform to look for the train again, but still there was nothing to see. He smirked as he saw Hallie had stuck the Coke back under her armpit so she could stuff both her hands in her pockets.

"Are you happy you moved here now?" he asked.

"Right this second?" she said.

He shrugged. "Yeah, and all the other seconds too, I guess."

"I don't think I've decided yet. Is that fair?"

"Sure," he said. "It's still new."

She grabbed the Coke and held it away from her waist as she unscrewed the top. It only exploded a little bit so she shook the soda off her hand. She offered it to Jacob first, and he accepted.

"I haven't decided if I like who I am here," she said. "If I know who I am here."

"Hmm." He handed the bottle back to her so she could drink. "You don't seem that different."

"Yeah. Life just seems to work differently here and I wonder when I'm going to stop looking around at everyone and start feeling like I'm part of those lives now too."

"Maybe you have to decide if you want that life first," he said.

"Well, how do I know?"

"I dunno," he shrugged, "but I think maybe you just will."

She nodded, chewing on the corner of her lip. Her mouth twinged like she wanted to say something but she changed her mind. She pulled the flask back out of her pocket and gestured at Jacob to come block her from the growing group of passengers. She poured the flask into what was left of the Diet Coke, scrunching her nose the whole time. Then she dropped the flask back into her pocket and took a swig from the bottle.

"Disgusting," she said, handing the bottle to Jacob who held it up for a toast.

"To my bladder: hope he can hold out until 2nd Ave," he said, squeezing his eyes together tightly as he drank.

"Oh god, me too," she said, "I'll try not to think about that."

They saw the lights coming around the corner then, so they took a step back and pulled their collars up to brace themselves from the wind as the cars blew past.

"But doesn't it just sound like a good idea? I mean, if you had to make a fake business wouldn't you want it to be something that's cash heavy," she started counting on her fingers, "hard to trace, constantly mobile, no consistency in consumer or customer base, I mean it's like ideal."

The three of them stood out on the balcony, sweltering in the July heat even though it was after midnight. Still drinking, now vodka in the wine glass, she continued: "I can't think of anything that would be better, right?"

The boys were leaning over the railing, looking down at the passersby: heading to the train, walking to the bars, enjoying a midsummer night out. Andrew shrugged.

"And in New York where it's really hot and people are constantly sweaty and yeah, people do buy those ice creams, I've seen it. I've even bought one in Manhattan. I've just never bought one in Bushwick because the trucks are never stopped, they're always driving around and I've never seen anyone stand out in front of them and stop them like they do in California. I feel like when I'm at home, I see them all the time and I see kids run outside of their houses and, like, wave them down. I've never seen anyone come out of an apartment building and wave them down. I've seen them stop for people on the street but I've never actually seen anyone run after one. Jacob, tell me I'm wrong."

"I can't. But I can't tell you you're right either."

"Okay so there you have it. It's the perfect conspiracy theory."

"You need to get laid."

Confetti

Harry Clough

A battle-scarred mother kisses her son,
Nodding and cheering him on as he propels
A toy boat onto the duck pond;
A tremulous launch into a tiny ocean.

An anxious child sits bowed, trembling-lipped at dinner
As words and threats are hurled around like confetti,
Crushed underfoot, pounded into mud by high-heels,
Forgotten by the bride and groom, remembered by him.

A nervous boy kisses another nervous boy for the first time
In cubicled secrecy, listening out for the jury
And when an older boy walks in, they quickly break apart,
Guilty smiles on our faces.

An emerging teenager succumbs to his first love,
And when his heaviness of heart threatens to over-
Balance the toy boat on the duck pond, he falls
Back in a cloud of confetti, leans into a mother's hug;

I am the one who waits.

A nervous man kisses another nervous man.

Kapok

Yuqing Zhuge

In the Kingdom of Flower Sea, each tree has its own name. When spring comes, everyone here endeavours to be crowned the King of Flowers. Their faces are upturned, their arms outstretched, and they are dressed in colorful red, pink, and purple clothes.

The static spring turns into a world as colourful as a rainbow. The cuckoo hides in the branches of the peach tree; begonia, hyacinth, and auricular primrose quietly peek out from behind trunk and wood; the willow trees sprout a promising array of light yellow young leaves; the green wheat shoots sway in the breeze.

I, the Kapok Tree, silently watch the lovely show of flowers, but I'm unwilling to enter the competition. Some trees think I am a failure, for I bloom for so short a time, but not me. That's who I am. My flowers die sooner than any of theirs. I only have fifteen days to bloom. At the end of my flowering period, the red flowers jump off the branches without hesitation, falling into the dirt. This is me; even if the flowering period is short-lived, it lives brilliantly.

Then, white tidbits of my soul dance all over the sky, unfettered, like cotton in the wind. That's who I am – unobtrusive, uncompromising, free.

After the long spring rain, I saw the neighbouring bamboo shoots sprout from the soil. I couldn't help smiling as I watched them rushing out to feel the vitality of spring, like children embracing a sunny day.

'Hero, your flowers are the most flamboyant of all in bloom!' Peach Tree beside the bamboo shoots applauded.

'Thank you! As you know, my time is short, so I must live as ardently as possible,' I answered, looking down at a critter climbing my thorny body. Everyone here calls me Hero because of my special experience.

Once, I had been a general in the countryside, where I led people to repel the invaders. But a turncoat ratted me out to the enemies, and I was captured. They tied me to a kapok tree and tortured me for fifteen days, during which my blood seeped little by little into its trunk.

I still remember the invader who bashed in our territory. He wore a white turban on his head. Sjamboks soaked in salt water rained down on me, whipping and ripping my flesh. Blood trickled from my wounds. My body trembled, a frail cry breaking out of my mouth. I clenched my teeth in an effort to keep the sound of my pain from reaching their ears.

Their leader was even angrier when he saw how tough I was. He wanted to hear my cries. He threw away the sjambok and pulled out a long sabre, silver and shining. I gulped, and felt my toughness disappear.

He leered at me, holding the sword.

The silver tip pierced my chest. The cold, burning sensation of my wound gnawed at my will to live.

The man forced the sword deeper into my body.

There were no words to describe the pain. I only knew that I was going to die. He yanked the sword free, and my blood poured out like a flood. I slumped against the kapok tree. The trunk behind me reddened.

I raised my head, seeing the tree full of kapok flowers, as ardent as fire. As my eyes grew heavy, death inched closer, and a smile crept onto the corners of my lips. *Maybe I can exist in this world in another way.* With that thought, I no longer felt scared. The soul inside me clamoured to get out. It detached from my body like the white tidbits of cotton departing the kapok, pollinating and wedding to the tree.

I became a kapok tree. My trunk is full of thorns and my branches stretch out as far as they please. There are no leaves when the kapok flowers bloom, but they regenerate after the blossoms are gone. When the flowers bloom they open blood-red, a flame for all to see.

After the florescence, petals fall into the soil, never looking back.

I am different from all the others who bloom throughout spring and summer. I only have fifteen days to flower, one for each day of my torture. So every spring, I burn to life like a roaring fire.

I prefer being a bright light in the dark of night, not being blown out but providing hope, warmth, and protection.

I do it all the time.

Last year, a girl cried under my branches, leaning against my trunk.

'I'm a failure,' she wept.

'How so?' I asked.

'I can't find meaning in my life.' She sat on the ground, looking up at me with tears streaming down her cheeks. 'I'm an orphan. No one cares about my existence.'

She buried her face in her hands and a whine escaped through her fingers.

'I care.' I shook my branches. A kapok flower fluttered on her shoulder. 'Look!'

'Although the kapok has only fifteen days to live, every day it burns heartily. Lots of tourists come here to see them during those fifteen days.'

The girl stopped crying, staring at me with watery eyes.

I continued. 'You can do it too. I look forward to the day when you've bettered yourself. Life is hard, life is tiring. But you can live for yourself and for your own happiness. Success is not something short-lived.'

A smile as beautiful as a lily crept up her cheeks.

I don't know whether the girl really understood what I meant. But when she was ready to leave, she took with her a piece of me.

A Cat Called Charlotte Perkins Gilman

Sam O'Brien

The man you swore you'd marry is finally moving out, god bless him. You were starting to worry that he didn't have a backbone. He's shuffling about your room blinking the wet out of his eyes, like a schoolboy awaiting public flagellation. He picks things up and then throws them down again in a grief-ridden frenzy, attempting to distinguish his things from yours.

'What you're attempting to do right now is – by definition – impossible,' you say, sitting upright in bed, your legs crossed primly. Hair parted neatly down the center. Pious and un-human, like a medieval painting. It is fascinating how little evidence there is that you are falling apart.

'I'll do my best,' he says. A t-shirt that you used to sleep in from a 5K that he ran lies limp in his arms.

Well, according to his logic, you get the house. All three floors, with the high vaulted ceilings, the big airy kitchen with the glass walls, tucked at the edge of the Alaskan wilderness – you alone signed the lease, put down the deposit, purchased and subsequently neglected all of the now-rotting plants. But he hasn't slept in his own bed since the New Year; your toothbrushes stand upright, blue and pink, in a Mason jar by the sink. You fall asleep each night to the leafy alders swaying and stroking your windowsill, his palm lodged in the space between your shoulder blades. You wake up to the sound of ravens bickering, the smell of him frying eggs for two.

It had always seemed as though he were the most liable for hurt: he is younger, hopelessly romantic, with bright blue trusting eyes. He writes you bad songs, plucking them out for you on the ukulele, while you smile at him from behind a pair of tightly-pressed lips. But you've gotta hand it to him: while you are busy waffling and making bad jokes and dodging serious questions and begging for him to hate-fuck you in a McDonald's bathroom, he knows – long before you do – when it's time to call it good.

In the early days, you told each other all sorts of marvelous things, whispered them back and forth in ecstatic bursts while coiled in a heap on the floor. Breathless. Your future spooling out magnificently before you. Your faces flushed with wine. I love you. I want to marry you. Buy a house. Raise a cat. A cat, who you mutually agreed to call Ernestine Hayes, after the Alaskan writer whose words you fell in love with just as you were falling in love with each other. You'd imagined you'd take turns reading her *Blonde Indian* and *The Tao of Raven* before bed, even though she is a cat and probably wouldn't appreciate postcolonial literature. Each wild declaration, each heady, farfetched promise, came up organic as if pulled from the earth. Stone by stone, you two built something together out of moss and rock and worms and dirt.

He studies the 5K t-shirt for a moment. Now he is crying. He is a man. He is a boy. He wants to be held. You are stoic. You are a girl – no, you're a *woman*. Your breasts spill out of your shirt like cantaloupes. You hold a mortgage. You refuse to hold him. He folds the shirt into the box. You watch from the window as he loads up his truck and drives away.

As summer bleeds into fall, it is surprisingly easy to return to the normal cadence of existence. You use your home as a staging ground for Real Life, dumping the contents of your backpack out on your bedroom floor, slipping in and out of different floor-length skirts, dragging a comb through your hair and braiding it down the side, sucking down an espresso, and smearing rouge on your lips. You step out the door: a woman with a paying job and a nearly paid off mortgage. With no one watching from the windows, listening on the other side of the wall, you can continue performing yourself.

And who says you can't get a cat? You're an *evolved* woman. You're at the phase in your life where you can invite friends over for things called 'dinner parties' and serve them home-cooked meals on reusable plateware, wine in big bulbous glasses as opposed to red Solo cups. You are chipping away at a graduate degree and sometimes you talk about starting a garden. A cat, at this point, seems inevitable. Sure, you can't name her Ernestine Hayes – that version of your life has been dead a month and counting. So you'll call her something else: Charlotte Perkins Gilman. You loved *The Yellow Wallpaper* in high school because it was frightening – unreal yet somehow plausible, as all good stories are.

September smells of rotting fish. One day, you march out into the damp air and to the -local animal shelter with unusual vigor. You watch from one side of a glass window as the new litter of kittens wriggle and play and fold their bodies around each other. And then you see her: she's sat to the side, eyeing the others suspiciously as they tug at yarn balls and leap at beams of light projected on walls. She is sleek-bodied, a metallic gray, with big yellow eyes. Her face is narrow and pointed and her ears are so large that rather than stand upright, they collapse under their own weight, folding over the side of her head. She makes the other kittens look trite. She is perfect. You pay in cash, stick her in a tote bag – her little head poking out warily – and walk a mile home in the wet, fishy air.

Meanwhile, your parents live on the opposite end of the continent. You left five years ago for a job, a dream, and some fodder for a memoir – something that they'd never quite forgiven. With a punishing regularity, they call you up:

What happens when we're old and sick and dying?
Well it's a good thing you aren't. Old, sick, or dying, that is.
But what happens when we are*?*

When the man entered your life, they softened a bit; love was a sort of prison that they could understand. But now that the man is gone, they have resumed the practice with full force.

The man you thought you would marry went to a lot of therapy in his youth to help him process his parents' divorce. As a result, in the immediate aftermath, he uses dumb phrases like 'healthy separation' and 'toxic codependency' and has made it a personal policy of his to block your number, unfollow you on all social media accounts, and never contact you again. When he cleaned out your shared bedroom, he did a thorough job of taking what's his to avoid the painful bureaucracy of a prolonged breakup.

But you are an expert at prolonging things. The day he left, you managed to filch a page from the notebook in which he wrote bad songs for you, and other things, apparently, that he hadn't bothered to share. The page contains his unnervingly neat scrawl: *J. is like The Lightbulb. You can't recall life without her.* And then, several lines down, in a different color ink, the scrawl becomes more erratic, littered with cross-outs: *J= lightbulb. Bright enough to blind you.* And then several lines past that, the writing is barely legible, but when you press it up against the wall, smooth it out, and squint at it, you can decipher: *J. is a lightbulb. She'll convince you that you need her, even in a nightless Alaskan summer. Even when you're better off just lighting a candle.* Now, you leave this out on the night table on his side of the bed. You pick it up and crumple it and uncrumple it every now and then, looking at it for a long while, staring at the blue-and-black etchings on the page. You have memorized the way the letters look upside-down, sideways, tilted on an angle. There is a pattern to it. A gestalt. You could conjure the image in your sleep.

In October, it is still warm enough to keep the windows open, but only if you are brave. The rain is horizontal and as a result, the inside of your home is often, needlessly damp. One night you roll yourself a thick joint. You crank open the window closest to your bed and slink beneath the covers, keeping a single hand postured on the sill, flicking ashes into your woodsy expanse of a backyard. You are bleary-eyed, musty, and recumbent when Charlotte Perkins Gilman mounts your bed in a single, startling spring. There is something patently gremlin-like about her, you realize, her yellow eyes bulging like Gollum. That night as you fall asleep you imagine what it would be like to lift her up by the haunches and toss her out the window. To tell her, as she howls into the night air, that you love her. To sit and watch her fall three flights before landing with a satisfying splat in your spice garden.

November contains moments of rare and terrifying beauty, moments where the rain halts and the sun shines and it may as well be summer. Moments where the sky turns an orange-pink at three in the afternoon. One morning you take a walk through a clearing in the forest, your skirt hiked up to your knees. Light everywhere. You are struck by a strange, floating sense of euphoria, and it is that feeling, that *feeling* that you'd better grab tight quickly, because soon it will be gone. You arrive home to find Charlotte Perkins Gilman sitting on your stoop, accusing, a gaping wound in her head. It oozes a yellow-green pus and there's crust along the sides. You sprint to the vet – guilt makes an Olympian out of you – Charlotte Perkins Gilman swinging in a tote beside you. But the vet is unperturbed, disappointingly so. He patches her up with gauze and sends you off with a complimentary pouch of ointment. A domestic horror like any other.

In December, the darkness comes so suddenly that if you don't rush to catch the sun when it first peeks out from beneath the cloud cover, you might just miss it entirely. It is easy to neglect the simplest of things: brushing your teeth, washing your hair, applying ointment to Charlotte Perkins Gilman's frothing wound. One such day, you peer out your window in your clothing from yesterday and find that night has descended, before you'd even had the chance to live. But there is a certain hopefulness to this: if the day never started, then it never happened. This thought fortifies you. You could go on sleeping like this, you think, when you turn to find Charlotte Perkins Gilman lying in a heap on your bedroom floor. You prod the lump of her back, confirming. And the feeling is this: no disgust, no horror, not even a tinge of sadness. Instead: resentment. No one prepared you for this. Your mother never lectured you on how to deal with the festering corpse of your neglected pet. Besides the ground is frozen and unsuited for a proper burial.

But lucky for you, there *is* the internet. An online forum suggests that when a pet dies, it's best to store them in the freezer to avoid rot – the fact of death being hard enough without the smell. At first this suggestion appalls you, a dead cat bumping up against your frozen mangoes and Cherry Garcia and other things you don't eat, but could. But then you remember: you have one of those industrial-sized freezers for stockpiling fish and meat, a relic from the Alaskan man whose life was once woven seamlessly into yours. He left it behind because he couldn't fit it into his truck but also because for him there will be other houses with other freezers and other women to fall in and out of love with. He possesses a beautiful optimism that allows him to believe in such things. You don't hunt, you don't fish, and if you believed in other possibilities the way he did, you might start to wonder what, exactly, you are still doing here. But not right now. Right now, you are a woman with a dead cat.

So you retrieve a pair of rubber gloves from the cabinet beneath the sink, two opaque garbage bags, flattening one bag on the concrete step to use the other as rolling paper. Swaddling Charlotte Perkins Gilman like a botched loaf of bread, you release her into the freezer. She drops with a thud and you slam the lid shut, with a rush of dizzying relief.

As winter dissolves into spring into summer, the house is no longer a staging ground for Real Life. The house is where life begins and ends. Your days become a series of quiet in-betweens, moments where it's just you, trapped within your same four walls, collapsing into yourself now that there's no real life worth living. The moment of silence before bed, once you've tossed your phone across the room and flicked off your bedside lamp, the moment between waking and awareness in which his hand would have, in another life, reached across the sprawl of sheets for your torso. Sometimes, something grey and formless slinks across the perimeters of your vision. Sometimes the cat flap will swing, sometimes the tapestry lining the wall will begin to move, the patterns contorting themselves into something nimble and feline. Sometimes, you feel a yellow-green light icy on the small of your back. By June, the sun barely sets and neither do you; your life becomes one long sleepless night.

Years pass in this fashion. Your body grows softer and rounder. You still jump and yelp turning corners in your home, not that anyone's around to take notice of it. Your parents grow old and one day, your father dies. It is expected, in the way that age and illness prepare you for such things, but also not at all. You are consistently bad at predicting the ways in which your life will come apart at the seams. And your mother takes to calling you daily, sometimes twice. *I've lost my best friend,* she explains through sobs, a human woman fully cleaved in two.

And so you quit your job, decide to move back home, as perhaps you always knew you would. The guilt of moving so far away so long ago – creeping up behind you for years – now coils itself around your legs and envelopes you. It is surprising how easy it is to uproot your existence when all you have holding you in place are logistics.

And it is not until the night before you are set to leave, your whole life pressed neatly into two suitcases, that Charlotte Perkins

Gilman manifests herself to you fully. She appears to you like a silhouette, but the opposite; instead of the absence of color and light she is the absence of form: grey, crackling, and boneless. She sits on the edge of your bed and for the first time, you find her phantom presence calming. She will remain a crystalized corpse in the freezer for the house's next inhabitants to find. It's her house now. Tomorrow you will go home, be a good daughter, be someone worth loving. You've made loads of promises in your silly little life. It's high time you make good. Your grieving mother waits.

Stray

Daniel Dicks

Though you walked those same worn cobbles
Embraced by a sudden wind
That you still recognised by taste,
And when you stopped a moment
At the cathedral, you last went to with him,
The saints still looked down on you
With their worried, weathered faces,
Charlie still begging on that corner,
The river still kissing its way past the same bridges,

When you stood outside that house,
And the familiar yellowed light
Flickering on in your bedroom window spilled
A warm streak across your face, you found
The space between curtains,
Drawn suddenly closed against you
By a stranger's silhouetted hand.

Sea Monster

Harry Clough

His little pinafore hung off his shoulders
Sand-stained and dampened from the
Murmuring shoreline's swell
He sat clutching mother's straw hat
Fat fingers curled around the frayed brim
Worms revelling after a storm

He watched as Mother went swiftly away
Towards the shivering lake's edge
Smiling as she went
Laughing over her shoulder
'Watch Mummy swim to the end of the jetty'

Mother plunged after wading to her thighs
On the bank he exploded with laughter

As the water crashed around Mother's vanished form
His glee died as the ripples
Died beside the dropped hat that
Wilted and dissolved as well

Until a distant disturbance in the water

Brought them both gasping up for air

Ferromagnetism at Fairfield Ave

Brevin Persike

Gregg used to have high hopes. But sometimes high hopes lead to depressing realizations, like the one he is having right now at a four-way stop at the top of the hill on Fairfield Ave. Today is his thirty-fourth birthday, and that in and of itself is not the depressing realization, though it is part of it. But for now, he isn't even aware that it's his birthday.

With his foot on the brake, he looks down at the train tracks, the river, and Fairfield Bridge, trying hard to ignore the monstrosity that is the paper mill running the entire left side of Fairfield Ave on down to the river. It's here he remembers hearing something about innate gravitational forces in human bodies, bringing them face to face with what they fear. There aren't any cars to be seen, but he can't get himself to release the brake. Slowly he beats his head into the window – one, two, three, four times. He stops. He peels his head from the glass and lays it onto the steering wheel. After a few seconds, he sits up again.

Fucking Chernobyl, or something. Shit, that's right, he was gonna watch *Chernobyl* on HBO. Anyways Chernobyl, that's what he's reminded of every day at this stop sign – death and loneliness and grey-brown snow. A wasteland. No cars are on the street, only five sets of railroad tracks, three of which are permanently blocked by rail cars no longer in use. Gregg thinks the mill and its grounds would be a good place for a war: lofted ceilings, hideouts, big machinery. The tow motors could easily be militarized, though, their gas tanks would be an easy target, if WWIII ever reached the woods of Wisconsin. The whole city already has the feel of a disaster site, why not make use of it? They used to say this city had the most bars per capita - or was it per square mile - in the US? Gregg doesn't remember and it really doesn't matter either way, but now all the former patrons are in hospitals and old-person homes, or, uh... assisted living facilities. Whatever they are, that's all this town has: old people and a highly pollutant paper mill, both of which promote the smell of gas and hazardous waste.

This isn't where Gregg thought he would be by now, thirty-four and living his greatest fear. Someone told him once – though he doesn't remember who, or if they were at all credible – that what you most fear, you unconsciously desire, but this life doesn't feel desirable. His car is still motionless at the four way stop. His eyes follow a red light flashing in the sky, briefly lighting up the chemicals being pumped from the smokestacks. Gregg remembers his ma telling him, 'Your father breathes like a fucking sleaze stack.' Ha, what the hell, Ma. It's 9:27 p.m. according to the clock in Gregg's Prius.

He musters the energy to let his foot off the brake and allow the car to roll down the hill and through the intersection. The car's momentum is enough to pull into the lot and up to his parking space. It isn't really his, but nobody else would park in the very last spot, a half-mile from the entrance. Gregg thinks about all the time he spent on this street – it seems to him that he spent his whole life walking Fairfield Ave, past the mill and along the bridge. He wouldn't end up there, he thought to himself then, he would make it out to live and work - possibly even thrive - somewhere else. The life he saw there was hell, everything about living like that would be hell. And he wasn't wrong to think that. Everyone knew or, well, fuck, was probably related to someone who worked at the mill, and they all knew it was hell. How in the fuck, he asks himself, did he end up here? Didn't he read something about minerals and magnets and how your body makes decisions for you, so you'll eventually end up where you belong? It probably didn't mean anything. Too heavily tied to determinism, anyways. Gregg doesn't spend a lot of time thinking about fate and free will, but he does know he isn't interested in determinism.

After high school, when most of Gregg's friends went to work at the paper mill, Gregg distanced himself, told himself he was better, he would do something valuable, not just press buttons and follow orders. He went to college and said he would take control of his own life and, after years of setbacks, he eventually got a degree in Environmental Journalism. But he's no better for it. He works shifts for a major pollutant without having written a draft or even revised the title of the so far nonexistent exposé he'd intended to write as an excuse for taking the job: Secrets of the Interior: A deep dive into rural America's manufacturing problem.

He doesn't want to be here. There never was going to be an article. He knew that then and knows it now. But there's something about this place that draws people back: magnets. Seriously.

He knows he's fucked things up. Probably irreparably in some cases. He isn't here to be recognized as 'a good guy', but maybe working here, feeling stuck and ashamed, is in fact his penance – the time he could give in lieu of the prison sentence he was never required to serve.

The lights on his blue Prius shut off as lifted trucks and stupidly loud Jeeps pull into the lot, exhaust pouring into the sky.

'Well let's do it.' He has to talk his hand into opening the door.

'Fuck.' He grabs his lunchbox and backpack with his right hand, dragging them across his seat, and slings the backpack over his shoulder as he pulls himself upright. Gregg's feet never make it off the ground as he shuffles towards the entrance. He fumbles with the buttons on his flannel with his free hand, which shakes from some combination of evening coffee, disdain, and the cold breeze off the river. Eventually, it ends up buttoned, albeit off by one.

Gregg watches the snow blow across the street and further yet, across Fairfield Bridge, dissolving into the river below. This whole place draws attention in the same way a car crash might. Gregg thinks of flashing lights, people crying. Up ahead, more flannel shirts step out of their trucks and onto the sidewalk. They all remind him of war: marching in unison, backpacks over shoulders, lunchboxes in hands, red hats with confederate flags on them worn backwards, like troops parading through a recently bombed street. Many of them actually went to war in Iraq or Afghanistan or what have you. But Gregg's less concerned with that and focuses more on the next civil war.

Maybe a war would give him distance from this town that he continues to be pulled back to. Even if he'd likely be on the losing side, the side that prefers pacifism and bans on assault rifles, he'd at least be forced into a new existence. Gregg read about WWI and WWII and came to understand it as 'not too great an experience', earning the same evaluation as a camping trip with his father on his ninth birthday, when all he wanted was a model X-Wing Starfighter. It was a moment of absolute reality, wherein the two of them wound up lost, wet, and hungry. A series of mistakes with tent construction, map reading, and general poor planning resulted in them sitting in a rowboat without worms, casting empty lures into a swamp-like lake, while talking about the problems with the US going to war in Vietnam as rain poured over them, dampening the whole experience. Gregg knows it wasn't quite war, but it wasn't totally dissimilar, as it were. War, Gregg thinks, is about action and people being forced into action, and that might just be what it takes to get some separation from his hometown. And when it's all said and done, maybe Gregg would be able to place himself among people who are not Scott – or aren't even like Scott – his partner, who he sees up ahead. Scott sees him too. There's no avoiding him now. He stumbles into Gregg on the sidewalk, wearing the same sweat stained, tattered rag of a T-shirt he does every day: 'Hillary's a Whore', it says. Scott's kind of an idiot. Not just kind of, actually. Some people don't need qualifiers in front of their adjectives. That's the kind of thing Gregg learned at journalism school.

'Don't talk to me Scott,' Gregg says, as he says most days. He means it. He doesn't want to hear Scott talk.

But Scott always seems to think it's a joke, or an invitation. Scott rants about 'that N-word Obama.' Gregg tells him that he needs to stop living in the past. But Scott keeps talking, so Gregg thinks about being elsewhere, somewhere where the sky isn't filled with pollutants and the people are smart or know some things; maybe that's too high a bar. Gregg just wants to live somewhere where people aren't assholes. Ha, that's pretty funny actually, Gregg thinks, picturing assholes with legs and arms. In college, he was gifted a tongue figurine with legs and arms that would dance like a bobblehead; later, he acquired a penis statue – with legs only – to sit next to the dancing tongue.

'Not comin' in yet?' Scott interrupts the dancing figures in Gregg's head.

Well, here we are, at the entrance to hell.

'Oh, uhm, no,' Gregg says. 'Tell Rick he can leave, I'll be in shortly.' He continues past the entrance and toward Fairfield Bridge.

Gregg is well acquainted with this bridge. When he was in elementary school, he would fish off the bridge with Willie and Ido. Willie would teach them cuss words like 'tit-flicker' and 'bastard' and 'dickhead.' Ido was quiet, but laughed at the words and used them sparsely at school. Gregg always asked what they all meant, or said, 'Can you use it in a sentence, please?' And Willie would say, 'Don't be such a tit-flicker! Get it now?' Tit-flicker – what does that even mean?

From ages thirteen to sixteen Gregg walked along the bridge every day on his way home from school. He would stand against the railing and stare down, imagining his body hitting the water and having it shatter around him like glass. But he was on a tight schedule back then. His father was home by 3:00 p.m. every day and only gave Gregg until 3:20 p.m. to get home from school, which ended at 2:55 p.m.

Gregg had all of his father's agonizing rules memorized. No shoes in the house. No crumbs on the table. No unwashed hands touching table-like surfaces, walls or doorknobs – 'You doorknob!' Gregg hears his father's voice yell. No eating outside of the tile-floored area, and then it must be done over a plate while seated.

Silently, often flawlessly, Gregg followed his father's commands. They were always running through his head. Except for the days he would scream and yell, 'Fuck you, you fucking tit-flicker!' and run away. But even then, he would come home and wash the dishes, wipe down the counters and take out the trash. 'You really think that's clean? Do it right the first time, son, you'll be better for it.'

Gregg still has to fight off his father's voice in his head saying things like, 'I wouldn't do that if I were you, sonny' or 'Do you really think I won't find out you masturbated on the couch? Doorknob.'

After chores and homework were done, he would walk to the bridge and convince himself that nobody would care if he jumped off. He never tried it, though. A girl from his class did later, maybe when he was sixteen or seventeen. But it didn't work. It's not high enough and the water's too deep, so it ended up just being a really cold swim. She said she was happy it didn't work. It wasn't two weeks later she ended up stealing a car, before getting caught in Illinois or Indiana or something like that. Then she stabbed her brother fourteen times with a steak knife after the authorities brought her back.

Gregg checks his phone for the time – 9:49 p.m. – and thinks he probably should go back. Instead, he sets his lunchbox down, holds onto a lamppost, and lifts one leg over the railing of the bridge, then pulls his other one over. The wind presses against his back and vehicles begin to roar out the parking lot. 'Yer gonna get fired, Doorknob. Yer blowing yer life away.'

Fuck you, tit-flicker.

Gregg watches the snow drift off building tops and melt into the flowing water below, then turns back and looks at the building – its brick walls crumbling and slowly being replaced with corrugated metal siding.

He's reminded of *A Quiet Place* and *Station Eleven* and *Call of Duty* and the way bridges and forests and abandoned warehouses are conducive to surviving an apocalypse. Gregg thinks he's built to survive catastrophes, though he realizes that's probably irrational to some extent. Even John Krasinski can't survive an apocalypse. But he did break rule #6: Don't be a hero. Gregg is no hero. He knows that. He's reminded of that every time he sees Fairfield Bridge.

The night of his little brother Henry's graduation party. The car crash. The flashing lights. The bridge lit up like the Fourth of July. The paramedics with their blankets, the police with their accident reports and sobriety tests and what have you. Somebody from the other car died at the hospital. Gregg wished – still wishes – that was him. Instead, routine distracted driving – no gross negligence, no DUI or DWI. Just a single night in a jail cell and a five-hundred-dollar fine. It wasn't even bad. He wished it was worse.

The magnets brought him home as punishment. And now Gregg doesn't even remember her name – the distraction. Haley or Kaylee or Katie – one of Henry's exes – who was giving him a blowjob at the time of the accident. They probably could've waited, Gregg thinks now, until they found some place to park. Or maybe just not done it. She was his brother's ex after all. If that had crossed his mind back then, maybe none of this would have happened, maybe he would've been too caught up imagining her mouth on his brother's penis. But that's all past. It did happen. Probably the fucking magnets.

Gregg presses his head into the lamppost next to him. He thinks about the hypothetical civil war. But it wouldn't have to be a war. It could just be an apocalypse. He thinks he's prepared for that. They say traumatic events and catastrophes change a person's memory, realign a person's magnetic makeup. Maybe he wouldn't be brought back to this godforsaken place. Fuckssake. Chrissake. Birthday Cake. Ha.

It's Gregg's birthday today. Thirty-four, now. 'Happy birthday to me, happy birthday to me... ah, what the fuck.' He pulls himself off the railing and back to the sidewalk, picks up his lunchbox, and walks to the front door of the paper mill. Thirty-four and still thinking about things that happened when he was twenty. When he gets to the entrance, he sees himself reflected in the glass. His eyes look tired. His face is speckled and wrinkled.

Fuck it. He walks past, back up the hill on Fairfield Ave to his blue Toyota Prius, parked in the very last space in the lot. Gregg thinks of gravity and the magnet theory again. He's gonna get fired now. But maybe that'll rid him of the magnets. His Prius isn't on yet, he could turn around, show up a few minutes late, get a warning. Instead, he presses the power button to the Prius and pulls out onto the street. He stares out the windshield and imagines he's flying through space in the X-Wing Starfighter as the snow blows into the windshield, illuminated by the car's headlights. There is no war to fight, but Gregg's in space, on some sort of rescue mission for the rebel cause.

Purgatory

Andrea Mejía Amézquita

The first time I heard Mami saying the name, my abuela tried to comfort her with a pat on the shoulder. It was during one of those picnics we used to arrange at the family mausoleum. Abuela would lay a picnic blanket by the vault's black metal gate, but often she and Mami ended up sitting on a nearby bench that Tio Nicodemo had put up for family visits before he passed away.

The mausoleum was a grey block at the very back of the town's cemetery. It was guarded by two defaced cherubs and shrouded in wild ivy and thorns that twisted around rugged pillars. Sometimes I peeked through the murky windows, trying to guess which of those crypts would keep my grandma, my mother, and me. I liked to think that once I passed away, I'd play in the cemetery forever, and my children and their children would arrange picnics to spend some time with me and my mom, grandmother, great grandmother, and all of my uncles, aunties, and cousins slumbering in that city of stones and bones.

I also played among the tombs sometimes, hiding from the undertaker, because he always scolded me. 'Don't rip the flowers!' or

'Don't step on the graves!' or 'Leave that candle, kid!' I never understood why he was so cranky all the time. To me, those tombstones and mausoleums were not as solemn as he made them look. Instead, I thought of them as the best hiding spot to eavesdrop on Mami and Abuela. There, I could listen to those whispers they dared to exchange when they thought I was gone.

I heard Mami's trembling voice. It was sweet and choppy, as if lacking air.

'I won't call her, Mom. She's a child. Let her play.'

'You're always trying to protect her,' Abuela said as she pulled an apple out of the picnic basket. 'Someday she'll have to come to sit with us, so she won't forget...'

So I wouldn't forget what? Was she talking about the name Mami recalled with so much fear?

Mami didn't reply. Abuela always had the last word. Puzzled, I looked back at the mausoleum to seek that dreadful name by the family crypts.

My abuela once told me our house dated back to colonial times, and that our family had lived there ever since. The square rooms and halls seemed to have sprouted around a patio with a stone fountain that only knew the taste of water when it rained. The house's squeaky doors complained in the mornings, and the wooden beams seemed to let out melancholy cries when we left to visit the cemetery on the weekends. The ghostly sounds of the house often scared me, but Abuela told me to ignore them. They were our home's 'old-age aches,' she said, as if it were alive.

I used to play alone with a soccer ball in the house's hallway. I liked to kick it against the wall, so that it would bounce back to me. On rainy afternoons, I imagined the thumping of the ball was the roar of thunder in the sky. One day I kicked the ball so hard that a piece of drywall seemed to fall. The house was old, I knew that, but

I never thought it was *that* old. I ran to pick up my ball, afraid that Mami or Abuela had heard something. However, I stopped a yard away from the fallen piece when I saw it tremble. Cautious, I approached the dark object and realized I had hit a moth. It fluttered on the floor, helpless, because I broke one of its wings.

I looked at her with curiosity, waiting for her to fly or surrender, to stop spinning on the floor and give in to death. It was an ugly, fuzzy, brownish insect, so I wasn't that affected by its imminent fate. I hunkered down and, mesmerized by the creature's struggle, stroked its broken wing and felt it crack like a dry leaf under my finger. Then I heard a gasp behind me.

'Don't touch that!' Mami yelled with a mixture of horror and disgust.

'It can't fly,' I replied, indifferent, as I backed away and watched my mami taking off her sandal to end the insect's agony.

'Hey! Hey! What are you doing?' I heard Abuela's raspy voice as she peeked out of her bedroom door. The uproar must've woken her from her afternoon nap.

'I'm killing that bug. Black butterflies are a plague,' Mami said. My abuela laughed slowly, displaying a nearly toothless smile that reminded me of the skeleton statues watching over some of the oldest and most elegant tombs in the cemetery.

'You're an idiot, aren't you, child? A plague! Moths are the souls in purgatory. You know every night I light a candle and dedicate the Lord's Prayer and Hail Mary to them. They visit our world to return the favor and look after us.'

Mami looked at the insect, unable to hide her disgust, but she didn't reply. She put her shoe back on and returned to her bedroom. I stood watching that poor soul still struggling to fly, wondering whether my abuela's prayers would be enough to repair its broken wing. Once again, I kicked the ball, disregarding that poor moth or 'purgatory soul,' as Abuela called it.

One night, I dreamt I was flying above the town until a giant moth appeared and flapped its colossal wings to throw me into a black pit where my house used to be. I was awakened by the roar of a thunderstorm, the growl of the monster moth. The downpour flashed its white light as the house howled and the wind rushed across the hallways. I recoiled in my blankets, trying to find some comfort to restore the dream that fear had snatched away from me.

I called Mami, hoping my voice would rise above the tempest. Maybe she was asleep, so she couldn't hear me. I sat up and in a fleeting moment of courage, ran to the open door of my room to call my mom again. Standing under the threshold, I peered into the corridor, hoping to catch some movement. Instead, I noticed that my abuela's bedroom door was ajar, barely lit with a shivering light. I assumed she was still awake.

I walked to my abuela's bedroom and knocked on the door. The house let out a lethargic squeal as I entered the room. The wall in front of Abuela's bed was adorned with portraits of saints, angels, and virgins. The effigy that stood out the most was a crowned Virgin set in the center of the wall. In front of her, my abuela had put a kneeler where she used to pray. The Virgin Mary rose above a sea of flames, from which the faces and bodies of half-naked men and women sprouted like fragile flowers in a blood-drenched field. They stared at the sky with their hands clasped in a gesture of unforeseen hope amid the chaos that consumed them. Before the figure, Abuela placed a couple of candles and a vase with white roses that perfumed her room.

She was praying a rosary on her prie-dieu. I didn't say anything and just stopped by her side to stare at the figure of the Virgin and the souls in purgatory. Abuela tilted her head to invite me to pray with her. I obeyed and knelt by her side. The dancing flames of the candles struck the faces of the tormented souls with their light.

Behind the Virgin Mary, the shadow of the Damned in the fire trembled the way Abuela said the souls squirm amid their scorching sins.

'Holy Mary, Mother of God, pray for us sinners, now and at the hour of our death. Amen.' Abuela concluded the last mystery before turning to look at me. 'Don't forget, my child: dedicate one of your prayers to the souls in purgatory. Those poor creatures left this world with many unresolved issues. You lend them a helping hand with your prayers. And best of all, they're very grateful.'

'Are they like ghosts?' I asked.

She shrugged.

'In a manner of speaking. Ghosts have unsolved issues.'

'I don't believe in ghosts.'

After I said that, Grandma paralyzed me with her grim and rigid gaze. The fear that had woken me came back to hit me with lightning precision. I knew I could no longer retract my words, explain them or, in any case, apologize for what I said. Abuela's voice rose above the sizzling flame of the candle.

'And do you believe in God?'

'Yes,' I replied. That's what I was taught to say when someone asked me that.

'And in Heaven? And Hell?'

'Yes, yes,' I said as an automaton, still fearful of the severity of my abuela's interrogation.

'Life after death?'

I remembered my games at the cemetery. I wished for life after death to exist, so I could play in the graveyard forever. But one thing is to wish and another to believe things are the way you want them to be. I remained silent, unable to reply to my abuela's question, maybe out of fear or maybe because I didn't know the correct answer.

The last time the three of us visited the cemetery on the same side of life, I heard once more the secret name on my mother's lips. Mami looked down whenever she said it. Abuela, on the other hand, remained silent yet expectant. It was scary when she looked at you like that, waiting for you to say what she wanted to hear, unless you wanted to suffer her indifference. For a month or so – in case you were lucky – she turned you into the ghost whose existence you denied, until she was merciful enough to remember your face in her prayers and welcome you back to her side.

'I mean we should stop this,' Mami said, barely looking at her mother's eyes. I knew that was the wrong answer. Abuela shook her head vehemently, tight lips, and nostrils wide open. Her burning eyes were full of tears of rage. Every day she looked more like those marble skulls that would guard her eternal dream.

'I can't believe you're saying that about an innocent baby. I can't believe it.'

'But, Mom, I can't go on like this! I don't want my daughter to carry my burden. For God's sake, we should take her to the park, to school, to make friends! She shouldn't waste her time here. What kind of childhood is this?'

I had never seen Mami like that, overflowing with courage, a voice so clear, sincere, and strong. I think I never saw her as convinced of something as she was at that moment. But the power in her gaze faltered as soon as Abuela began to speak.

'You're killing me, child... You'll kill me with your words. Who would've thought I'd give birth to such a selfish, heartless, cruel creature? Why would God punish me with someone like you?'

'Mom, please, it's been fifteen years! Fifteen years grieving for a death we've already mourned! It was an accident!'

'You're talking about your daughter! An unborn, unbaptized creature!'

'*My living daughter* is wasting her childhood surrounded by dead people and in a house that's about to fall apart!'

I stifled a scream when Abuela slapped Mami. With that single blow she wiped away all the bravery that bathed my mother's face with an unforeseen glow of life. My mom just touched her cheek and looked down again with tearful, ghostly eyes. Abuela lowered her hand and let out all her anger in an exhalation, not because she was calm, but because she managed to regain control of the situation. Once more, she was in charge.

'Our family has lived in that house for generations. No one will leave,' she said sternly. 'My parents, their parents, and their parents before them lived and died there. And so I hope that will happen with me, with you, and with the generations to come... Family sticks with family, and your family is here!' she said, pointing at the mausoleum's gates. 'Be grateful I forgave your sinful youth and was even willing to receive that unborn girl into the family. Show some mercy for her, and at least let her know she's not suffering alone.'

Mami nodded and gave in to the embrace Grandma offered her. I turned my gaze to the dirty windows of the family mausoleum, looking for the crypt of that sister who, now I knew, was sleeping in one of those dusty recesses.

The Plaza Hotel

Ceilidh Michelle

Holed up in bed in the Plaza Hotel, using my coat as a blanket. The sheets were too thin and the bulb was dead in the lamp. I guess it was supposed to be glamorous, this small room, this little battleground.

Victoria, British Columbia was a hotbed for unemployment, poverty, addicts, homelessness. Willy and I hadn't even meant to wind up on the island. We had been wandering from city to city and just got stuck there. By the end of it we were strung out and useless. We jumped in a taxi, escaping unpaid rent and the wrath of drug dealers, and went to the Plaza Hotel.

A grated-faced German man was behind the front desk in the lobby. He asked us, 'You vant to book za room by hour or veek?'

'Weekly,' we muttered, putting down a few precious dollars and lugging whatever we still owned, a battered guitar, a garbage bag of clothes, into the elevator. Someone had taken a piss in the corner. Somebody else must have come behind him or her and sprayed a big old bottle of bleach on top of the accident. The air in the tiny elevator was thick with fumes. My eyes filled with water.

We pushed the second-floor button. The first-floor button had been ripped out to reveal wire guts and the third-floor button, also ripped out, had been replaced with a chocolate candy now white with age.

The elevator jolted up to the second floor, doors screaming open to reveal filthy windows looking over Chinatown. We could see the roof of the lobby below us, a rusty satellite dish strewn across it like ruins on the moon. Also beneath us was a bar called Monty's Exotic, a strip club.

Willy and I smoked cigarettes on the windowsills of our room, listening to the different layers of chaos – sediment of sirens, bedrock of drunken conversation. The noise from the strip club beneath us rattled the room like seismic activity. The dancers stayed in the hotel with us. They wobbled up and down the hallways in their high heels, looking for dope. The police broke it up at three in the morning and everyone went home but us.

Our room had been painted jaundice yellow. When I put my face close to the surface I could see bandages and odd hairs trapped beneath the paint. The floor had been covered in loose squares of mismatched carpet but beneath that was the original rug, rose-pink and cigarette burned. Fake flowers decorated a broken dresser. The lamps were screwed down and we had to bang on them to get them to flicker to life. The toilet flushed when it felt like it. The phone didn't work but there was a CD player chained to the nightstand. We found two dirty condoms under the bed.

My favourite part was the eagle. Someone had ripped a picture from a magazine, a big bald eagle flying through the sky. Shoved crookedly into a plastic frame, it hung on the wall like a piece of fine art. You could see the cardboard backing and the tattered edge of the page. It was wonderful.

Willy took me by the hands and danced me all around the room. And I thought, this is just another season.

We met George the next morning. He'd been living in room 204 for a decade. But he'd just found out, along with everyone else, that the hotel was being shut down at the end of the year.

George was fuming when he got the news. We could hear him crashing around his room, pacing, screaming, 'Fuck City Hall!' When he surfaced in the lobby, his shoulders hunched, his face buried beneath a wiry grey beard, whoever was behind the desk shouted at him to find money for his room.

'It's all City Hall's fault,' George barked back, leaning crazily against the desk. 'I been here, you been here, it ain't fuckin' right man. I'll come back in an hour and give you ten bucks and a case of beer.'

'Your room is three-fifty for the week, George.'

'Fuck City Hall! We should all go down there and tell 'em. We can fix this place up and they won't have to close it.'

I admired his hope, his tenacity. But seeing solutions in the wrong things had also gotten me into trouble. That's why we were here, Willy and I. That's why we were all here. I watched George huff off into the elevator, grizzled and thin, a huge bag on his back like he was homeless already.

At night, there was always some dancer complaining about a 'violent, shouting man in room 204.' People assumed he was in there with somebody else but he never was.

I was walking out of the hotel towards the bank and ran into one of the men who worked at the front desk.

He was going my way, so instead of awkwardly walking along and pretending we didn't know the other one was there, Sammy said, 'You and your boyfriend are the musicians?'

'That's right,' I said and we began strolling along side by side.

'How'd you wind up at the Plaza?' Sammy was a bear of a man, thick black beard, always in the same outfit of black sweatpants and black t-shirt with the sleeves cut off, doughy arms carpeted in course hair.

'Long story,' I said, which was the only way I knew how to answer for my life.

'Hotel is a fucked up place isn't it,' said Sammy. It was not a question. There was no question about it.

'Yeah.' I tried not to think too hard about it. I was young. There seemed to be no consequences.

As we walked past the cafes and fast food places, convenience stores, the lights and traffic, Sammy chatted away. 'Plaza used to be an old speak-easy back in the prohibition. This might sound like complete bullshit but it's true, swear on my mother. Sometimes I start work early, like five in the morning? And I'll take the service elevator down to the basement. Sometimes I can actually hear glasses clinking and people laughing.'

He looked over at me to see how this hit me. I said nothing so he kept talking. 'The bouncer at Monty's, he's no pansy, this guy. He had to go down to the basement once at *night*. He comes back up shaking and scared, I mean really scared. He said he saw a *skirt* whip around the corner down there, like an old fashioned dress. He said he heard a woman's *voice*.'

As he walked Sammy parted people like a sea. I practically jogged alongside him to keep up.

'But that wasn't the thing that pushed him over the edge,' Sammy said. 'You ready for this?'

I told him I was.

'The next time he went down to the basement he came back up *running*. He ran out of the building fast as he could and never came back. He told the guy at the desk that he'd seen the ghost of a hanged woman.'

I didn't mind the stories. It felt right that my surroundings matched the contents of me.

'I'll be sure to stick to my room,' I told Sammy.

Somehow we at least had jobs – he was washing dishes in the pit of some restaurant and I bounced around from diner to cafe. We had enough money for the room, a few drinks, cigarettes, some food, whatever.

The nights were rough. There was usually a dancer in a nearby room getting beaten up. The savagery of a man throwing a woman against the wall, the smashing of a fist to a face, the crying, the begging, it all came into your dreams.

One night, a whole flock of dancers were partying in the room next to us. By six in the morning they were still going strong. The walls were so thin I could hear them snorting their dope, the long wet snuff. The tin can stereo vibrated our headboard. Their spiteful laughter was hard against the quiet night. Willy and I lay in the sheets and groaned.

'That slut needs to get fucked *up*, that bitch needs to learn her place,' one of them hollered to the others.

'You tell 'em girl,' the others crowed back.

They made a seedy chorus, the leader singing curses and the others echoing back a defiant refrain.

Willy lost his patience and punched the wall. '*Shut the fuck up!*' he bellowed.

I laughed into my pillow. It took a lot to get Willy to snap and I appreciated a good outburst from time to time.

The ladies all began reacting at once, screaming and hollering, and banging on the walls.

Poor Willy just put his head under the pillow. He was usually a stoic force beside me, letting me drag him here and there and never complained. He barely spoke. He barely existed at all.

One night, Willy and I decided we deserved a little break and met a man in the parking garage. Willy handed over a few bills and the man said, 'Be right back, be right back.'

He didn't come back, of course. I sat yelling at Willy in the parking garage. The concrete bounced around the names of our petty losses, an infinity of shit. I told Willy he was a fucking loser. I had been counting on him to lift me up, to get me high. What was the point of living like rats if we couldn't even have the sweetness of being stoned? I hated Willy. He made me feel a prisoner and a fool.

We wandered back through the little city of Victoria, the trees sparkling with white lights, tourists beaming their broad American smiles against the backdrop of the Pacific Ocean.

Willy and I limped along. Recognizing our people leaning in doorways or under awnings, we waved to each other. We were the only ones who could see.

When we got back to the hotel we decided to go to the strip club to cheer ourselves up. But we must have missed everything – by the time we got there the lights were on, the stage was empty, and the only thing that lingered was the smell.

Robert came to the hotel a few days later. He had a grey fish face, dead eyes like nickels, colourless hair and walked with a hospital-issued cane. Always out of his mind on something, he staggered back and forth in front of the hotel's entrance from morning until night. I kept my distance. There was no coming back from where he had gone and if I kept back maybe it wouldn't catch me, and I could come away clean.

He had a little posse he wandered around with, three of the worst degenerates I'd ever seen. One of them was a rat-faced woman who wore a black pleather outfit. She had a teenaged boy with her, maybe her son or a young lover. He had a blotchy purple birthmark covering the entire left side of his face. Robert also kept a man by his side like some kind of bodyguard. The man was bald with jeans so tight I could see exactly what he was all about.

The bald man got kicked out of the hotel same night they checked in. He was busted smoking a crack pipe in the lobby. Sammy ushered him out, the rat-faced woman following along screaming expletives and gripping the shoulders of the birthmark kid, who clamped his lips shut and stared off into space.

Willy and I caught the tail end of this scene while coming in from the street and we fled to our room before it sucked us in.

Of course the bald man was back the next night, due to the Plaza's rent-to-anyone-as- long-as-they-had-cash policy. When we saw that weird crew roaming around again, Willy and I ate some cannabis cookies for protection and climbed into bed with our paperback novels. Sammy had given us the cookies out of pity because Robert and his cronies were in the room next to ours. They spent every night crashing around as if they were performing their own depraved theatrical, swearing and hollering and singing along to the radio, shoving each other into the walls.

Willy and I clung to each other, stoned. It was in the night when the darkness closed in that we reached for each other, our defences lowered only in the small hours, and only when we were alone together did we touch, grab for each other's hands, let our gestures become gentle, kind.

On the other side of the wall I listened to the waves of television commercials and Robert pacing back and forth, slurring and moaning and holding court. Suddenly it sounded like he collapsed, his body smashing and then sliding down the wall right behind our heads.

The rat-faced woman began screeching, insistent as a fire alarm.

'Sit him up! Sit him up, goddamn it!' the bald man shouted. Rat-face kept screeching until he shouted again, 'Calm down, you crazy fucking bitch!' Then, 'Robert, hey buddy, sit up man, you did too much. He did too much. Can you hear me? Robert?'

There was a hacking, coughing noise and then, 'He's good, he's good. Everyone just fucking relax.'

We lay in bed just listening to it all, Willy drumming his fingers on my ribcage, both of us staring up at the ceiling.

I ran into Robert the following morning. He wore bloodstained hospital pants, his face greyer than ever and slick with a toxic sweat.

'Hey sweetheart, you got change for this dollar?' But he dropped the coin, his eyeballs
rolling.

I headed inside while he scrambled to pick up his money off the ground. The sky was heavy with coming rain, the wind from the marina sharp as blades.

Behind me I could hear Robert telling one of his friends, 'C'mon into the hotel, I got the *best* crack.'

Sammy sat behind the front desk. He turned up the radio.

There were a couple of evenings where the sky was so clear you could see the horizon of blue mountains all the way to Washington. I perched on the windowsill of our hotel room blowing bubbles into the night.

'*WEEEEEEEEEEEEEEELL, I've been drinking all day...*' wailed an old man from down on the street corner, smashing out some savage blues on a haggard guitar.

The neon hotel sign blazed right beneath my legs, so close I could count the bulbs. The big red dragon gates of Chinatown roared up from the street as if they were going to set fire to the little city.

My bare feet hanging loose in the purple air, Willy playing his guitar behind me, it was almost peaceful.

'Don't fall,' he warned.

When we left the hotel we took as many pillows, sheets and towels as we could carry. No one even noticed.

The Air Between Breaths

Doug O'Hara

She stood at the edge of a parking lot bordered by woods, preparing to hike for hours, weaving through dodgy trails and steep inclines. The early morning peeked through a swirl of clouds and jet streams in a golden haze of sunlight amid a steel-blue sky. A chill numbed the tips of her fingers. She tucked them in her pockets and rocked back and forth, admiring the cluster of aspens and firs. For a moment she closed her eyes and imagined he was inspecting the car or retightening their water jugs for the hundredth time or at the visitor center inspecting the brochures and maps before hastily hoarding them in his back pocket. A smile slipped at the corners of her mouth, awakened by a glimpse of the past. Her hand opened gently, waiting for his fingers to intertwine with hers – to hold him as they began their long hike up the hillside. She glanced down at her hand, as the brisk air streamed through her fingers. It felt like before – if only for a moment.

She began on the path as it zig-zagged up the trail, dodging the pockets of sunlight sizzling on the dirt. Drops of sweat stung at the edges of her eyes. She felt like an ant under a magnifying glass. Her lungs constricted and each breath burned down her throat. She untied the red and black flannel around her waist and stuffed it in her backpack as dry grass crunched and cracked under her boots like a graveyard of bones. She winced and imagined seeing his face – beaten and broken in the hospital bed.

It had been a year since he passed. Months on the road away from home, away from the constant reminders and pitied looks – the countless conversations avoiding any mention of him. Everyone assured her the grief would pass, that it would just leave one day, that it would all get better. But it never did. The pain dulled but never left, lying dormant at the corners of her heart and awakening when she least expected it.

The path wound around an arrow-shaped boulder then climbed through patches of shrubs and tall grass. Her t-shirt soaked and latched to her skin like glue while wisps of hair clung to her forehead. Her teeth clamped shut and she wanted to scream. She never liked hiking... but he did.

After he passed away, the pain was soothed by friends and family. Bouquets of flowers, random visits during the day, late-nights reminiscing about old stories as if he were merely away on a trip, or even spontaneous get-togethers so she didn't have to eat alone. For a time the pain lessened. Then the months passed.

Eventually, everyone went back to their lives, went back to their same daily routines as if nothing had happened. As if there was an expiration date for grief – for missing him. The phone calls dwindled. The flowers decayed. The dinners stopped. Everyone moved on while her life stood still. His absence echoed through their apartment and her body paid the price. It began with unexpected migraines that soon turned the apartment into a sullen dark cave. Then came the dry heaving, numerous times hunching over the toilet until there was nothing left while she begged for it to stop. Food tasted stale, sleep became a thing of the past, dirty clothes stacked into a landfill of laundry, and the four walls of their bedroom whispered and tormented her. The doctors blamed it on depression but the less she took care of herself, the better she felt. It was closer to him in some way. He existed in the pain.

Countless nights, she woke scared and confused, reaching for him, yearning for the safety of his body. Her eyes tricked her into seeing his head sunk on the pillow, or his legs tousled and hidden in the covers as if he were playing some strange game of hide and seek. But then reality would settle in. The pain would rise from its slumber, mutating into anger as it plagued her body. She would kick off the covers, and thrash on the bed, slamming her fists against his pillow and screaming at the feigned hope he was still there. For a moment it felt good.

The silence echoed and his spot remained empty.

Hours passed as she hiked further up the canyon. A shallow stream coiled around an oasis of agaves and white-petaled flowers. She pulled off her boots and socks and dipped her reddened feet into the water. A slight piercing freeze followed by a soothing relief. She retrieved the red and black flannel, dipping the sleeves into the water and wrapping it around her neck. She remembered that November night in New Hampshire, and how their feet dangled off the dock. How he sacrificed his flannel and wrapped it around her like a scarf when all she wanted was the simple retreat of the fire inside. The warmth of his embrace as she snuggled into his chest. Daring her to dip her feet in the water and her pride succumbing to his wistful challenges. And the ultimate prize of getting pneumonia the next day. How she would gladly freeze under those layers of blankets if it meant he were next to her now.

Around a bend on the trail, she reached a door-shaped tunnel cut through the ridge. Her breath quickened as she leaned against the rock, welcoming the respite of shade from the sun's ire. She lifted his baseball cap and wiped the sweat pooling at her forehead. Her fingers glided over the ripped brim, and she grinned at the grease stains smeared across the side. His hat. The same dirty old thing stained with motor oil and transmission fluid as he would wiggle on the concrete floor, worming deeper under her car, fixing the latest breakdown. He wasn't a mechanic, but he knew his way around cars. Like most things, he had a deep interest in how they worked and a deeper curiosity for trying to figure them out. But she never was good with cars. A veterinarian didn't have to be. Sterilizations, mending broken bones, even heart surgery, sure, but changing motor oil? Refilling antifreeze? Forget it. She nestled the hat back on her head and continued through the tunnel.

A thin stretch of rock loomed over the canyon, scattered with patches of yellowed grass and naked juniper roots writhing in the sunlight. As she reached the top, the untamed wind burst through the clearing and kicked clouds of dirt against her cheeks. She coughed dryly and tried to swallow down the burning pain as if she just vomited. In her backpack, she fished out her bottle and drank some water, conserving the last few sips as her throat begged for more.

Across the canyon, ribbons of heat danced above a range of copper-stained mesas and plateaus, dotted with pine trees and bushes. He would have liked it here. He would have dangled his feet over the cliff and told her about how the rocks smoothed, or how long the canyon stretched, or what year it became a national park. Spurting out random facts was a talent of his, and another thing gone from her life. If he were here.

The canvas in front of her dulled, and that sudden happiness, if only for a moment, faded.

She grasped the flannel closer and smelled the barley and hints of spiced pumpkin from his brewery. When was the last time he wore this? Labor Day? The baseball game at the park? At breakfast that one Sunday when his parents came over? What did they have? Pancakes? Scrambled eggs? But when was that? When was the last time? The memories blurred. Her hands clutched the collar until her knuckles formed mountains of red capped with snow.

For a while she sat by the edge of the cliff. The range of mesas towered over the valley. She noticed the ground below, split like dry skin. On the top of the ridge, she was alone, exposed to the elements – tiny and insignificant to everything that surrounded her. The heat simmered over the canyon, and her skin boiled. She reached for her bottle and glared at the bottom where the last few sips had evaporated.

The pain constricted her throat. She tried to fill in the cracks, paint over them, reassure herself she was okay, but nothing worked: not leaving town, not quitting her job, nothing. The cracks only grew bigger until they became a chasm. A chasm that became deeper, and deeper as time went on.

Her mind raced to her phone. The voicemail. There was still that. Before she knew it, it was in her hand, tempting her to call, despite that her battery was about to die. It was a risk, a risk she was willing to take to listen to the thing she'd clung onto so many times. Each day, something was forgotten and most days, a waterfall of memories slipped through her fingers.

The way he complained about wearing a suit. The late nights at the brewery, dancing and weaving around the tables without any music. Flapping away the smoke from the oven and smiling helplessly as she reached for the takeout menus. His high-pitch singing in the shower when he thought no one could hear. At the edge of the Grand Canyon, miles away from any memory, he still found his way into her mind. It was never the big things, but subtle little reminders. The memories slipped, shrunk to the countless pebbles scattered across the canyon. She fought back the tears, gripping piles of dirt in her hands and closed them in a tight fist. For a moment she forgot how to breathe. Her lips quivered and she inhaled short, shallow breaths. Her chest trembled and pounded. She was tired of fighting, tired of suppressing the pain, just... tired.

She peered up at the sun, a ring of light glistening amid the afternoon sky as she twisted the golden band on her finger. A tear escaped and soon the rest followed, canyoning down her cheeks as the pain flooded her body. In the chattering of her teeth, in the rushing of blood to her ears, in the strangling grip of her heart.

It was no longer the memories that happened but all the ones that wouldn't. Their first dance as husband and wife. Feeling the joy and fear of having a baby. Playing rock-paper-scissors to figure out who had to change diapers in the middle of the night. Dropping off their kids on the first day of school and eventually off to college. Growing old together and spoiling their grandkids on Christmas. Being there when it was time to let go of a lifetime.

Her legs gave way and she collapsed to the ground, ripping at her hair, wanting to squeeze the memories out, wanting the pain to go away, wanting the piece of herself that died with him – the piece worth living.

She squeezed her fists and shouted relentlessly into the sky, imagining his face bruised and beaten as three tons of steel crashed against a tree. His last thoughts as he died alone. The cold touch of his lips as she kissed them one last time as he rested in the coffin, his stiff chest where her head used to lay, and the last suit he would wear – black with the blue tie he was saving for their wedding day. Her soaking up the last few seconds before the casket closed, a final image of the life sucked out of him imprinting into her mind. No goodbye would've been good enough. No final farewell. No last I love you.

Her face contorted with relapsing agony. The flannel latched closer to her. She glanced down at her wrists and watched her pulse pounding against her skin. Her eyes shifted to his hunting knife in the front pouch of her bag. The rush of opening her veins sent tingles down her arms to the tips of her toes.

She leaned over the cliffside and gazed into the beckoning abyss. The bottom seemed to summon her; to whisper to her – to welcome her. It would all be over soon. There were worse ways to go. It would be quick. A rush of wind, a nice view, then a welcoming nothingness. There were worse ways to go.

As she inched forward, a layer of rocks lurched under her boots and she stumbled, jolting forward like the first time she teetered at the edge of a diving board.

A swarm of memories flashed through her mind. Her mother hovering over her birthday cake as she lit the candles. Sharing a few drinks with friends at the brewery. The contagious giggle from her niece when she piggybacked her through the yard. Bouts of splashing and diving into the pool as the smells of chlorine and BBQ mixed in the air on a summer afternoon.

She dug her boots into the dirt and kicked backwards, falling across the ground. Her feet launched in the air, spitting pebbles over the cliff. She crawled away from the edge and sat cross-legged, rocking back and forth, the Colorado River snaking through the valley. White-water rafting with him, grabbing her as she almost tipped over, the rush and fright coursing through her body. The promise he made. The promise that he would always catch her, always be there for her. Yet she was alone, she was still here and that meant figuring out how to continue on without him.

Her arms shook as each breath grew shorter, fumbling over the other. In and out. In and out. The air between breaths felt like an eternity.

For a while she sat quietly. In the distance, a cluster of scorched trees edged the forest. Maybe the bark was charred, the forest floor rotted, and the leaves and branches stricken. But she remembered watching that nature documentary with him, nestled against his chest.

She grinned.

Eventually, life would grow back, never the same but something new.

I See You

Laura Hiermann

I can't see them, but I know they're there. I can hear them blinking, their lashes cutting through the stale air of my bedroom. I hate them. I hate, hate, hate them. I despise their stripping gaze. I pull my blanket over my head, trying to hide from them, but they tear through it. They always find me. No matter what I do, no matter where I go, they're always here, waiting for me.

I noticed the first one on a Sunday afternoon. He was small and I had probably overlooked him before. At first, I thought he was a bug. I wanted to rescue him and return him to the outside world, but when I moved closer, I was stunned. He was a single eye fused with the wall. He didn't move, yet his dark brown iris rested on me. I shook my head, blinked, stepped closer and squatted down a bit so that we were even. How could this be? He held entirely still, reflecting an augmented version of my own face in the black depths of his pupil. I was surrounded by a warm dark brown, like melting chocolate wrapping me in a sticky sweetness. When he blinked, I froze, but then he kept his perfectly smooth lid closed for a moment as if to nod at me, as if to say hello. I looked at him and he looked at me. His corner moved up to form tiny laugh lines and I smiled back at him and got myself a chair. We spent hours just looking at each other. I could pick out the almonds that were the exact shape of his eye and draw the golden mandala that the sun painted on his iris at around five p.m. I knew the exact spot of the oval-shaped dot on his lower waterline just a few millimeters from the inner corner and the curving of one lash that grew down, instead of up. I was anxious that it might bother him, but it didn't seem to. He always just stared at me with his curious look that said, *I see you*, and I answered, *I see you, too*.

The next few days revolved around him, always circling back to the moments I spent sitting with him, while all others were lost in a blur. His mere presence fulfilled me. Instead of being tired after work, I danced through my living room with him cheering me on. Instead of chickening out, he convinced me to send my photographs to contests and agencies. Instead of sleepless nights alone in my bedroom, I dreamed of flying on my couch under his protection. I lived for the moments with him, but hours spent staring turned into minutes, and soon we simply existed together. He became a silent observer. Always admiring. Always observing. Always staring.

It was another Sunday. I was in bed masturbating, climbing higher and going faster. My heartbeat rushed through my entire body as all my muscles relaxed, but when I opened my eyes, I saw him, icy blue on the ceiling right above me. I was horrified. He was staring down with his lid half closed, laughing maliciously, mockingly. My entire body tensed up. I tried to hide under my blanket to escape him, but he found me. They always find me. I took another look and his gaze pierced me like an icicle. I was strapped to my bed, paralyzed. Nausea swelled in my stomach. Slowly, he peeled away one layer after another, each ravaged line of defense allowing him to invade one more part of my body, spreading from my stomach, up my spine, around my shoulders; crawling up my neck and settling on it like slimy spittle, making me gag. And he still stared at me. His gaze never moved. I couldn't look at him for long. I couldn't hold his stare. I averted my eyes, shrinking further and further underneath his triumphant, self-aggrandizing stare. I ran out of the bedroom, seeking the warmth and comfort of melted chocolate and I found it, yet there was something else above the left corner of my TV, which definitely wasn't a bug. He was too big. The wrinkles around him replayed the same laugh as if he had been in my bedroom too, only there wasn't even a blanket to hide under, and the brown I knew so well did nothing. He'd turned me over to his friends.

I wanted to ignore all of them in the pathetic hope that they might just disappear. And I tried. I truly tried. But each time I entered either of the rooms, they were staring, belittling me, objectifying me. Every time I turned away, they were boring through my back. I tried hanging my colorful tablecloth, the one with the rainbows, over the eye next to my TV, and my niece's drawing over the one on my bedroom ceiling, but nothing helped. Whenever I walked into the room, the invasiveness crept up on me and tightened around my throat, and eventually I surrendered.

The living room, the kitchen, and the bedroom were haunted by their presence. I began to avoid them at all costs, stacking groceries in my hall, moving the kettle to my bathroom. I subsisted on ramen and ramen alone. I'd sit in front of the kitchen door thinking about his melted chocolate eye, the way he made my heart flutter, my skin tingle, and aroused the urge within me to dance and dance and dance, but he'd betrayed me.

It took me a few more days to find a new routine, but once I did, I almost felt at home again. And life continued as if nothing had happened, except my flat had shrunk a little. That was until I woke one morning in the gloom of dusk to find they'd invaded the hallway. There were four in the bathroom too, and seven in the bedroom, as well as eleven in the kitchen and living room.

Since then, their numbers have continued to grow.

They've spread over all of the walls, even the ceiling. They've invaded every inch of my life. I've made it through an entire week now, peeing under a towel and changing under my blanket, unable to properly shower and eat. The office has become my sanctuary. The cold, minimalistic rooms feel warmer than before, warmer than the place that was once home. My desk used to be equipped with the bare minimum of office supplies. Now it's a mess. Panties in the drawer, a dying succulent, my favorite photograph from Gillian Wearing's *Signs*, and millions of Post-its, but it's my mess. My coworkers stare too. Their gaze twists around my legs and up my ass, grasping at my boobs and licking at my neck whenever I walk past, but it doesn't bore through me. It doesn't go any deeper. My coworkers are nothing compared to them. At work, I can eat and nap. At the flat I can't.

It's almost four4 a.m. I'm hiding underneath my blanket and I listen to their lashes cut through the air, as their lids close, the barely-audible, creepy rustling when their upper lashes meet their lower ones, and the squelching when they open again. I have had enough and cover my ears, surrounding myself with a vacuum of white noise. Yet, their gaze still disgusts me and undresses me and torments me. I stay in my vacuum as black turns into navy turns into blue turns into grey.

The rising sun finds its way through the fabric of my duvet. Slowly, I move it down my face to peek out into the room. I'm convinced the one right next to the dresser wasn't there when I went to bed, and neither was the eye next to the light switch, but I don't count them anymore. I can't even distinguish all of them; they're everywhere. I pull my blanket over my head again and I want to fade away, escape them, but I have nowhere else to go.

Suddenly, something strokes my check. I turn my head and he stares right at me from the inside of my blanket, his lashes almost touching my forehead. For a moment I freeze, but then I'm back and I grab him and I squeeze. He feels soft and slimy, a little like jelly, and I squeeze as hard as I can. He pops and smears in my fist until he oozes out from between my fingers. I wipe off the pink, gelatinous mass in my blanket. I was so sure that they were bound to the walls, but the rules seemed to have changed. What if one grows on me? I want my life back, the ability to shower and change and have moments entirely to myself again. I haven't thought of it before, but now it's becoming clear, like a kaleidoscope finding its right assemblance. I head to the kitchen and for the first time I'm not rushed. I'm not in a hurry. I feel calm; I'm the calm before the storm. They, however, are nervous; they blink out of rhythm, irises hectically flickering from me to each other.

In the kitchen, I carefully consider all my options and decide on the smallest and pointiest knife I own. It weighs almost nothing, and if I didn't know it was there, I'd think myself entirely unarmed. But I'm not. I return to the bedroom and there he is, right above the bed. I look into his piercing, icy blue and he stares right back at me. Confident. Challenging. Absolutely powerless. He thinks he's throwing icicles at me, but he's not. Instead, I stab right into the black hole in his center. His lid immediately closes and there's not a single drop of blood. His eye behind the lid doesn't move at all. I'm not entirely sure I did it right. Maybe I'd have to stab harder, deeper. His lid stays closed as I slowly pull out the knife. He's entirely still and I can even tell where the wound is, a little bump where it should be smooth, yet I'm not convinced. I don't want to run any risks, so I carefully lift up the lid with the tip of my knife and there it is. Piercing, icy, dead blue with a cut where my face used to be. And I'm excited. The adrenaline rushes through my body and I keep going. I stab and stab and stab. Blue, brown, green, grey, and every shade in between, one eye after the other. Closed and opened lids, it doesn't matter, I penetrate them all with my pointy knife. Each time I feel the slight resistance when I hit their cornea, I could scream with delight. I work myself through the bedroom, strategically ridding myself of them all. The ones on the living room ceiling are the hardest to reach, but I get to them, climbing on chairs and the couch and the table. Nothing can hinder me. Nothing can keep me anymore.

I catch his terrified melted chocolate stare, but I ignore him; I'm on a roll, and I just keep going. I stab the penultimate one next to the fridge, then return to him. Still there, in my living room corner. When I approach him, I can see his fear. His gaze darts through the room, from me to all his dead friends back to me. He sees me coming and he knows what I've done, knows what I'm about to do to him. I approach him until I'm only an arm's length away. His brown eye stares at me and although he cannot speak, I can hear him pleading. He fills with tears that he squeezes onto the wall, where they slowly trickle towards the floor, leaving behind a dark trace. He's begging me not to kill him. Explaining that he never hurt me, that he never wanted it to go this far, that none of this is his fault. But I know better. *I* know that he betrayed me and invited the others in. I know that he exploited the trust I had in him. I can't forgive that, and I don't want to.

He's still explaining and pleading and begging when I lift my knife and strike. I can see the warmth disappear from his dark brown iris. No more melted chocolate. My chest tightens and a lump in my throat shortens my breath. The adrenaline is gone, and I am exhausted. My arm is tired and lifting it even one more time seems impossible, but the tingle of excitement still tickles the tips of my fingers. I walk into my bedroom, where the air is stale but silent. My head rests on my pillow. Nothing moves when I close my eyes. I am finally alone.

Choose Being an Actor

Rosa Barbour

I'd seen Jack performing a couple of times at Gray's School of Drama in Glasgow. I was enrolled on the Screenwriting course and he was doing Acting, so our two groups were occasionally combined for monologue workshopping. My own scripts, despite my best efforts, had consistently failed to translate well to the stage. Jack had never been selected to read my work, but when he performed my coursemates' pieces he emitted an authentic, compelling energy that seemed to alter the atmosphere of the room itself. Outside of class, I'd heard it rumoured that while some of Jack's peers felt galvanised by his stage presence, others had been left outraged when he'd told them, in no uncertain terms, that they were not matching it. It was for this reason I'd found myself keeping a distance from Jack on a personal level. Impressed as I was by his obvious talent, I felt reluctant to test his critical insight against my own precarious potential.

Our workshops were overseen by Russell, a young tutor whose recent appointment had generated a ripple of excitement on campus. Most of us recognised him as the director of a few edgy, low-budget plays that had garnered critical acclaim in London. After the last class, I'd noticed Russell and Jack talking with a charged vibration that seemed to imply something beyond professional admiration. And so, when Jack approached me a couple of days later to ask if I wanted to go for a drink, I registered the distinctly "let's talk shop" vibe of his invitation without surprise, but with more than a little intrigue.

We met at All Bar One on St. Vincent Street. The glittery, spacious venue contrasted quite spectacularly with that of my last extra-curricular outing: a date at an actors' dive with floors so sticky I'd ended up sacrificing my flimsy ballet pumps to the gods of improv and beer. Since that night, I'd spent my off-campus hours in isolation, drinking my way through entire bottles of Sainsbury's Malbec with increasingly maudlin velocity.

'I really like your scripts, Briar. They're funny. Dark, I know. But funny. I've been meaning to tell you that for ages,' said Jack. He'd just ordered cocktails, and his eyes were fixed intently on mine as he adjusted his long, lean body on the stool opposite.

'To be honest, they haven't been my best.' It was the truth, but as I spoke, I struggled to suppress a grin of pleasure and relief.

'Really?' said Jack. 'Or did the other actors just murder them?'

I exploded with laughter before I could stop myself. In-house bitching at the academy was often dressed up to the point of imperceptibility, and as Jack watched me, one sardonic eyebrow raised, I could tell he was pleased by the effect of his directness. Flushed, I raised my hands to undo the top two buttons of my coat. It had belonged to Mum, and as I lifted the light material away from my body, the soft smell of her bloomed into the air around me. Powder, with a hint of something green – verbena, I thought. Or vetiver. For a split second, Jack's gaze hovered over my bare shoulders and neck. His ray of warm appreciation seemed to encircle my whole being – not just the bare skin on display. In its glow, I felt sparklingly present, neither exposed nor appraised.

'No, your scripts are good,' he said softly. 'You just need the right actor.'

The unsaid lingered for a moment, then united us in a brief conspiratorial smile.

When our drinks arrived, I was reminded of classic cocktails from the silver screen – tall crystal glasses blown exquisitely thin, loaded with spirits and syrup and soda, the Maraschino cherries peeking through the dense ice-frost like pink clouds. Jack smiled at our waitress, laying a hand lightly on her wrist in thanks. As she moved to the next table, an intimate little smirk blossomed on her lips so suddenly it seemed to catch her by surprise. I wondered if perhaps I'd been wrong about the vibe between Jack and Russell. Rather than watching the waitress, however, Jack's eyes were now fixed on a well-dressed young man sitting at a table near us, with dark curly hair and thick, groomed eyebrows. As though sensing Jack's interest, the man glanced over, then quickly away.

We set about our drinks, and Jack began telling me about his upbringing in the Borders: siblings, dogs, and plenty of money, from the sounds of it. He spoke matter-of-factly, not self-conscious about his privilege but not wearing it on his sleeve either. I found myself imagining his parents as an upbeat, forward-looking duo; not prone to the dark bouts of depression that I'd been accustomed to with Mum, and which for many years I had thought of as a given among all parent-kind. I stroked the soft collar of the coat beside me.

'When did you decide you wanted to make a go of the whole acting thing, then?' I said brightly, sensing that Jack was on the verge of asking about my own childhood.

'I remember when I was about fifteen,' he said, affecting a faraway, misty expression, 'sitting in front of my mirror doing Jake G's monologue from *Brokeback Mountain* about sexual frustration, you know – bla bla, "high-altitude fucks", bla bla, "son-of-a-whoreson-bitch", bla bla, "you count the damn few times we have been together in nearly twenty years and you measure the short fucking leash you keep me on – and then you ask me about Mexico and tell me you'll kill me for needing somethin' I don't hardly *never* get.'"

He was taking the piss, but the delivery was electric – voice quavering, eyes filling with tears at the last.

'How do you do that?' I asked, laughing.

'You should see my *Choose Life*, sweetheart.'

'I can only imagine.'

'Actually, I'm talking bollocks,' he said languidly. 'It's nowhere near as good as the *Brokeback*. Thing is – with Jake, I fully identify. I've spent many a lonely night in my room wishing I was having sex with Heath Ledger.'

He threw a devilish glance over his shoulder, locating the raven-haired stranger who was now standing at the edge of his group of friends. Turning back to me, Jack sucked the cherry from his cocktail stick, his eyes hovering over my face as though checking the effect he was having on me. Aware once again of the rare openness of my own body language, I was almost tempted to believe that Jack was consciously extending his forcefield of sexual magnetism to welcome the possibility of my own attraction for him. And yet, when it came to his plans for my own fate, I maintained the distinct feeling that Jack had come to the bar armed with a different type of card altogether. One he had yet to draw.

The waitress arrived with a tray: two more tall cocktails, plus two delicate, bell-like Nick & Nora glasses brimming with a sharp mix of vermouth, rye whiskey, and Campari. According to Jack, the mix was called the 'Old Pal'– a riff on the classic Negroni that he had managed, with a persuasive little wink, to order off-menu. He thanked the waitress gracefully, and she floated off, rosy-cheeked and beguiled once more.

'Anyway, back to me,' said Jack. We both sniggered at his tongue-in-cheek naughtiness, pulling our drinks towards us.

'I think I could do good work, in theatre especially, maybe,' he continued. 'But there's no real nobility to why I decided to pursue acting.'

'What d'you mean?'

As Jack took a thoughtful sip of his Old Pal, I noticed that the man from earlier had now broken off from his friends completely and was standing a few feet away from us, 'checking his phone'. Jack, sensing his audience, sharpened his posture. When he spoke again, his voice had adopted the timbre and projection of a distinguished storyteller.

'Acting is the best way to gain access to life, I think. Getting up early, walking through a foggy city to a rehearsal studio where everyone's at a certain level of their game. Forget "what's your star sign" and pretending to be a tree; this is preparing for opening night at the Old Vic surrounded by beautiful men in luxe sportswear reading Shakespeare and swigging lemon water. Landing your first on-screen gig; people you've never met looking you up on YouTube to watch a homemade compilation of your sex scenes with a U2 song in the background—'

He paused. The man close to us had given up all pretence of not paying attention, and two of his friends had sidled over to join him. Jack grinned, angling his good side towards an invisible camera as he entered the final throes of his performance.

'Getting cast in some filthy Channel 4 series, corpsing your way through thirty-six takes with what turns out to be the love of your life, the director eventually getting annoyed but you still can't stop fucking laughing. Working hard, but having fun – creating something good, then celebrating it. Back to the Dorchester with your co-star, strawberries and croissants in the morning before press. Don't get me wrong, I know that's not every actor's life. But it is for the ones who make it. That's the life I'm after.'

Jack threw himself back in his seat and took a glug of his drink in a "darling, I'm spent" sort of way. His efforts were rewarded as the three men watching broke into rapturous applause.

'Choose life. Choose being an actor,' I laughed.

'Aye – choose being Ewan McGregor!' said Jack, holding his glass aloft between us.

I clinked him, then sat back, contemplative. The polished, dark-haired man took his opportunity, approaching our table and shaking Jack's hand in a comic display of awestruck deference. They drank each other in, and I had a brief, lonely premonition of how the night would play out. And yet, even as I watched, Jack was politely but firmly calling a halt on the proceedings, turning away from his admirer and back towards me. The man stood for a second, looking slightly dizzy, before drifting slowly back towards his friends.

'You're looking thoughtful,' said Jack after a pause.

'I'm just thinking about your definition of life,' I said. 'It sounds good. It sounds, I dunno... *present*. I'm comparing it to, like, countless days indoors, typing away, not eating properly...'

'Do you see yourself writing telly, then?'

I laughed, but the sound was short and mirthless. I stared darkly into my drink, disturbed by visions of 'writers' meetings,' large glass rooms full of people speaking over each other... the word 'brainstorm'. I saw the pain of my grief leaking into my work, then being held up to the judgements of others like it was fair game.

'Come on. It's your turn,' said Jack.

I looked up at him, searching for the false empathy I'd come to know and loathe in the expressions of others, but his face was sincere. It occurred to me that the showiness of his speech hadn't been about impressing the men nearby. He had wanted to make me feel comfortable enough to let my guard down. I swigged a fortifying belt of Old Pal, and took a deep breath.

'Well, okay. When I was wee, I used to sit with my mum at the kitchen table and tell her stories about my day. She was sad a lot, so

I did it to cheer her up. I used to do accents, improvise huge screeds of dialogue. She… well, she said I was good at it.'

I faltered, but Jack was smiling at me as though what I had to say delighted him. I continued.

'These days, I just feel so disconnected from that early incentive and… well, *support*, I suppose… that made me want to write in the first place. I don't feel like I fit, or that I have the right sort of drive. There's this girl on the course, for example. Lizzie. She's the whole thing, you know, top-knot, clipboard. Oversized fake glasses. She kind of reminds me of a character from *The Wind and the Willows* – an otter or something. A pretty, officious otter who's moved to the city to work in TV. Every so often we get taught about networking and she's like, you know, "listen, I spent last summer babysitting Helen McRory's children for forty quid an hour, don't speak to me about networking". In all honesty, I don't even like her writing that much – it's cold, it gives me a bad feeling – but every time I look at her I think, yeah, she'll make it. I mean… I think I can write. But the idea of me actually getting a script commissioned just seems mad.'

I trailed off, realising I'd been gripping mum's coat very tightly as I spoke. When I released it, the air around me flowered once again, sweet and gentle with the smell of her.

'It'll be hard, yeah,' said Jack, lowering his glass to the table slowly. 'But look, there's always room for talent. And *you've got that.*'

'Thank you. Really. But let's face it, it's the people like Lizzie who—'

'Don't get hung up on Lizzie. She'll get her foot in the door – you can betcha bahttam dallah on that. But do you want it enough? Because if you do, you'll smash the networking, and the pitches, and all the pish. And *that*, combined with talent, will get you there.'

I smiled, pressing my fingers to my cheeks. The cool condensation from my glass carried along my palms, calming the red flush that had spread across my face.

'Right, enough of all that,' I said after a pause. 'Back to your lovely cosy hame in the Borders.'

'Well. It's not as *Brady Bunch* as it sounds. At all. In fact, I'm *out of favour*,' said Jack wryly.

'Oh. Why?'

'Why d'you think?'

'Not supportive re: Brokeback?'

Jack sank the last of his drink and, for the first time, looked uncomfortable.

'Aye, keep schtum about that, by the way.'

'Yeah, no, sorry, I didn't mean to—'

'No, no. I'm not in the throes of angst about it. Done all that. I'm just keeping my trap shut from a "shrewd professional" point of view. Which is a heinous cop-out and betrayal to myself and the cause of course, but aye. I'm going up for Stanley in the Christmas showcase. *Streetcar*, they're doing.'

He leaned forward, drawing absent-minded circles on the table with his bare cocktail stick. I watched the tendons in his forearm moving in the candlelight. He looked at me without raising his head, the light dancing in his eyes.

'I think I could do Stanley,' he said contemplatively.

'I'm sure you could.'

He played with the cocktail stick thoughtfully, then snapped it in two.

'Those showcases are the ones people come to. The London contingent. *Mucho* importante. I'm loath to say it, but it's true. "Oh, the wildcard Scot we saw in Glasgow! Yes, we could have him for the barefooted peasant boy in *Poldark*."'

'You could do worse.'

'Too right I could do worse. Bring on the *Poldark* bit-part. Speaking of London – what do you know about Russell? Have you Googled him?'

'Obviously, yes.'

'Those plays were no small deal. Two of the original *History Boys* cropped up in one of them. Not Corden, thank Christ. Point is: lots of guys on the Acting course are bankrupting themselves to get something on at the Fringe next year. I thought, why not go to Russell with an idea for a one-man show. Get him to direct me in it. Bit of clout. Several corners cut. To be honest, I've already started working on him. Pretty much got him in the palm of my hand, the poor thing.'

I nodded. Jack's ambition was boundless, but it didn't alienate me the way Lizzie's did. He was hungry – and he was right to be.

'Yeah. It's a good idea,' I said.

He shook his head in frustration. There was some crucial point to the conversation I was still failing to grasp. Jack had dealt his card, and I hadn't even realised it.

'No – but what about this,' he said, his gaze unwavering. '*You* write something. Thirty minutes. Vibrant. Spunky. I'll learn it, get totally off-book. Then we take it to Russell. That way, we come to him with a full plan, and— what? What is it?'

I breathed in deeply, trying to ground myself, and caught another whiff of Mum's perfume.

'The thing is,' I said shakily. 'I lost my mum recently... about six months ago... and I— all I can think of is streams of unanswered emails, trying to pin down Fringe venues, rewrites—'

Jack looked at me with a simple, frank compassion: the very same expression that had moved me almost to tears the first time I'd seen him act. He put a palm to my cheek and I closed my eyes, his thumb claiming my tears as he drew it gently across my skin. He smelt warm, and spicy, like a high-end Christmas potpourri.

'Do this play with me,' he said softly. 'You can write something that reflects how you feel. And I'll act my arse off for you. I think it could be great. Briar, d'you know what? I think it could be fucking brilliant.'

Looking into the sparkling blue eyes that were all at once new, yet somehow familiar, I thought he might be right. He drew his hand away, and I sensed a charged, magical quality in the air around us. His momentary touch had left his scent all around me: clinging to my curls, tickling my face and neck, and conquering the last faint notes of vetiver (or was it verbena?) that had nestled for so long on my collarbone; on the collar of my mother's favourite coat.

Forrest Road

Becky Jane Grieve

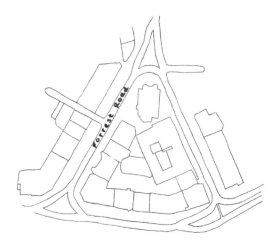

I want to talk to you.

Not bullshit talk about how your dad's business is getting on, or how you're deliberating whether to get a house cat.

But actually, talk.

I think, in fact, that my need to talk to you is the only thing that stops me from ending up with somebody who won't drink coffee after four in case it keeps them up all night, or makes me leave parties when they get a headache so they can take me home to thrust pathetically inside me a few times and then have the audacity to ask if I liked it.

That little off-licence we used to try and run to before 10pm is boarded up now, piles of rubbish stacked outside the metal grates. It's making me think about the time that you decided you were making us mulled wine in the middle of July. We drank it from china teacups while your hands wandered my thigh and we decided that it would be the perfect time to turn our living room into a blanket fort. I hate that my mind finds ways to loop back to you even when I'm begging it not to.

So I'm going to walk to this place, I have been walking to this place, every day. To talk to you.

It's not a particularly spectacular place, it's just your bus stop. It would have been great if it was some vast, melancholy lake or a particularly well-positioned park bench we both liked – poetic even. But it's not, it's just the stop on Forrest Road where you get the bus to work.

Right now, it's six-thirty: so, you're probably still in bed, not forcing yourself to get up before sunrise like I am in an obsessive attempt to 'beat the day', even though undoubtedly I'll just be nursing a coffee for the rest of it. But, eventually you'll get up for work at two – if you still work there because I know you really hated that stupid job.

We were never really on the same page, however much we tried to be. You'd draw lines where I would draw looping circles and after a while it just felt easier to rip the whole thing out and burn the book and all our doodles along with it.

Everybody knows that there's a window. Nobody talks about it, but there's a window. That month after the end of any relationship where there's still enough residual care there that you could probably phone them up at three in the morning if you wanted to – even if you shouldn't. Right now, our window's in need of a substantial cleaning because I muddied it with misdirected rage and you chipped the woodwork every time you silenced me with, 'you're impossible', rather than just letting us fight. So, you probably wouldn't take my call, but we're still in the window nonetheless.

That's why we need to speak – now, here, today – and I need to talk words at you until something clicks and I feel done with you. It's selfish, I know, but so are you for being so calm and internal about all this while I'm pacing the length of my bedroom and keeping the TV on to fall asleep.

I don't know what I have to say. I probably won't know until we're standing in front of one another practising the art of eye contact and I have to justify why I've been hanging around your bus stop. I'm angry about this, angry that I can't make sense of it all. It's not that ferocious heated anger – the one where my thoughts align themselves so clearly, tumbling into a formation that makes me feel ready to assassinate you verbally. It's that really cringe-inducing wet anger that makes me stumble over all my words dozens of times, trying to coax them into some form of coherence and getting pissed off that they won't come out right.

I wanted you, and I had you. Never all of you; definitely most of you, then some of you, and now absolutely none of you. And it was great at first – that's such a useless sentiment, of course it was, we wouldn't have wasted our time if it wasn't. But it was falling into each other on that saggy red couch and adding shots of vodka to our morning coffee and wondering if anyone else on the entire planet was quite as funny as us, and you said I was your favourite person which made me feel like you were encouraging the universe to incite chaos on all of those who weren't me. I am a wreck, a ruin, the last dregs of cereal at the bottom of the box, walking to this stupid bus stop, thinking about the time we sat across the living room from each other throwing Cheerios into one another's mouths, so enthralled in the spontaneity of it all. Until I left the empty bowls in the sink for too long to fester because I knew you'd do them for me, and then shouted at you for putting them away in the wrong cupboard and not being able to make the hoover work properly even though I'd shown you a thousand times. It was me, feeling shamed every time you'd ask, 'what have you done today?', because I knew you could never understand why sometimes just simply existing in it was hard enough. Feeling inadequate every time you tried to build a routine while I stripped myself of mine; adamant that I was being 'wild' and 'zany' and not just destructive and sad – like I knew that while you couldn't make me better, I could definitely make the two of us worse.

I am a monsoon of emotion and you are a stupid little puddle, always telling me we'll talk when I'm 'done freaking out'.

Maybe that's what I should tell you.

That was when I knew that things were ending. When everything about you started to strike a chord of anger in me that felt so animalistic and raw that I wanted to poke and prod you until you snapped and showed even a semblance of what bubbled so intensely in me that it was difficult to fathom how other people couldn't see it.

'It's called mania.' That's what my therapist said.

'Mania, interesting.' I'm clutching a coffee, I'm always clutching a coffee.

'There's a comfort in destruction; you've already decided on it. You've accepted the chaos, so if it all goes wrong at least you permitted it to be that way.'

But, we must speak, about that night, about *those* nights. The nights where I slammed the door so hard that it snapped the handle off and you told me you weren't there to just catch me and that you had broken yourself for me. *Broken.* What a word. And I told you that if that were the case you couldn't have been very hard to break. Then, you told me that I have a need to make everything great, and that it must be so torturous to assign such blame on myself and on you if it wasn't.

So, I'm not going to try to make you great. You are incapable of having a bowl of food without dropping some on your sweater, you grind your teeth in your sleep and it makes me want to shrug my skin off, you can't run to the bus without starting to sweat. I hate that you won't even register yourself for a dentist, and for the love of *god* do you need to sneeze ten times in a row?

That doesn't make me feel better. Being mean to you. I want it to, desperately, if it did I would list every single thing about you that ever bothered me and we could just talk about that. But you'll just brush it off as me being dramatic, and we both know that my ego is far too fragile for you to start producing a list of your own.

So I'm going to walk, every day, to this place. Sometimes I might come here twice, or three times, because I need to talk to you.

I chose this, I wanted this, and I defended it. There's nobody to blame apart from me and a stubbornness that decided I would feel more me without you. I played leaving you over and over in my head, so many times and in so many different ways that I almost decided that we'd already had the conversation; that you were mad and asking me where this had all come from and what you could change, and I thought you'd be begging and desperate for me, and as much as admitting it feels shameful, I wanted you to. I wanted you to be eager and thirsty and wilful. But, when we finally sat down and I told you that it wasn't working, all you said was, 'I know', and somehow that made me angrier because I wanted to duel and debate and dispute and disagree.

I know why. I know I was sparkly and magnetising until I became the girl that yearned for the night to never end. I watched myself light a match in you until you burnt out, coming home expecting my tribulations. And I lost interest in trying to convince you that things could be different when I knew that I was the one changing them.

But it was so easy for you. To leave. And now I'm the one walking to this stupid bus stop.

Running to this stupid fucking bus stop because it's nearly two and you might be there today.

We were a mess of flailing limbs and panting, and we drank each other up like some divine power was threatening to steal the glass.

I want to remind you that I'm great at magnifying things like this, at picking them apart until everyone's screaming at me to leave it alone. I don't think I loved you, not for the last while at least, hah – 'the last while', the last *year* of us, shuffling around each other, recanting the same dull stories we'd both heard a thousand times, kidding ourselves into thinking they were a valid exchange for intimacy. But I wanted to want you, and I told myself that it was at least better than leaving you and only having me would be. I have cursed myself enough for being this way, and you have also expressed how odd you found it that our feelings could match so perfectly one day and then bypass each other like two trains on a platform the next. Personally, I thought that was an awful simile and that you should perhaps get on your metaphorical train until you were passionate enough to describe us in the way that I am. From what I recall you liked me best this way, irrational, passionate. From what I also recall you hated it all regardless in the end, but this is my pointless rendition of events, and I need you to let me talk through this until I have said what needs to be said.

You won't be there. You're never there, but if I don't check it might be the one time that you will be.

What a cliché all of this is. What's my plan here? To write your name in a bubble of hearts and make a playlist of sad songs for you while I drink beer in my pants? I promise you I'm just as thoroughly disgusted by all of this as you probably would be. If this were some awful romantic movie – you know, the really cheesy kind we both hated – then this would be the part where I run to you, and you run to me, and we lock eyes and some dramatic music kicks in to indicate that this is the moment when we become each other's again. But this isn't that movie, and even if it was, nobody shows you the sequel where all their former problems come back to haunt them and then one of them decides they want to see other people.

I know that I'm going to reach this place and you won't be there.

Honestly, part of me never wants you to be there. It's so paradoxically dismal that I feel like after all this time I would implode on the spot if I did actually happen to catch a glimpse of you.

Am I the butt of my own joke now?

Bitter, pessimistic, sombre, sorrow. I make myself wince.

I'm nearly there now, I only have two minutes, and I can't miss you.

My dad used to tell me, 'home is where the heart is', and I thought it was just one of those things that people said when they didn't really have any real advice to offer you. But then I left that crumbling little flat and its saggy red couch and I realised that my new blank walls and unfamiliar room might never feel like home without you and that maybe no matter how much I scrape at the debris clouding that ever-shrinking window of ours I might never be able to see through it again.

Talk, discuss, descant, recite, argue, confer, consider, debate, deliberate, examine, review. That's all I want to do. Maybe we'll talk so much that I'll end up thinking I might love you again after all. But we must talk.

I'm at the stop and I can see your bus pulling up. The queue is cluttered with people and my eyes are trying to hunt you out.

Stupid, this is totally stupid. My hands are clammy and my stomach's groaning, like even it's getting fed up with me. I'm trying my best to scan the crowd. Tall man, short
woman, old lady, man with beard, and then—

You.

My entire body stiffens, and every word I have been preparing for you bubbles so vehemently that I think the entire contents of my stomach might flounce from my mouth.

It's you, I know it's you. And your bus is here. You pause, surveying the pathetic wreck I am, and I can see your eyes giving me an opportunity to make my move, to say what I need to say, to talk, discuss, descant, recite.

But I can't do it. My legs have fixed themselves upon the concrete. I am quaking, quivering, and teetering in this feeble, pitiful woe and all I can do is smile at you like a puppet.

You smile back, and the pity behind it fills me with that horrible wet anger. You turn to get on your bus, and I am still stood there, acting like all of this is just some random coincidence and that I haven't eaten, drank, and slept this moment ever since I started running to this stupid place every day.

The bus starts to pull off, and I am alone.

I want to talk to you.

Chasing Valor

an excerpt from *War Against Warlords*

Margaret Kroening

Kearn lifted the child's arm to run his wet rag over the bruised and lacerated skin and tried to blink away the lead weight in his eyelids. The abandoned cabin was cold from the relentless storm outside. Its black oak boards creaked as the chilly air shrank them and the wind pressed against the mossgrown walls. Rain had been hammering the old roof since before he had carried the girl's broken body through the door. It fought through the failing thatch to slide down the walls and patter noisily across the wooden floor. Cold damp clung to him, his clothes, his hair, burned in his nostrils. His fingers ached with it. Even the fire in the hearth struggled to burn because of the saturated air and sodden wood, and its weak light made Kearn strain to see his patient.

Exhaustion dogged every movement and pounded at the back of his skull. The last three days were a haze of repetition. Dipping his rag in the bowl of herbal solution had become maddeningly ritualistic. The acrid smell of poultices and raw meat filled the small cabin every time he unwrapped another wound to clean it. Beyond that, the ugly musk of decaying wood hovered like an oppressive blanket over his senses. Every breath was an assault on his empty stomach.

He shook his head and leaned back from the straw bed to disengage for a moment, to refocus. He cast his blurry vision up at the rafters and tried not to linger. Tried not to think about the hidden sword that the young girl had carried so far, that had brought her to this, and would cause her so much more harm for years to come. He tried not to compare her smiling face as she had rushed to greet him, just days before the raid, to the swollen and purpled version lying unmoving on the bed.

Best not to think about any of it just yet. Best to focus on the task at hand; grief wouldn't heal her. He bent back in with a sigh. Time enough to rest when his young patient was out of danger.

She had landed on her left side, and that leg had taken the brunt of the damage. The long bone in the upper leg had been a clean break, but below the knee her leg had grown to nearly twice its size even though he'd kept it elevated to reduce swelling. Those bones had been broken in several places, and he was concerned about how well they would heal. A limp would be a death sentence. She had to heal well enough to fight, and he worried as he looked down at the stitches of the flesh he'd cut open twice just to realign the shattered bones, that he hadn't sewn it back together well. He worried that he might have overlooked some muscle or tendon that might have been cut all the way through. Besides the lower left leg, there hadn't been much muscle tearing. Her left hip, on the other hand, was possibly fractured. Left arm also broken, but cleanly. Several ribs on the left side were broken as well, but her breathing was regular, enough. Her calf muscles would require extensive work to function as well as they once had... but within a few years, if she could stay hidden long enough to heal, she might regain enough mobility to fight for her survival when they found her again.

Kearn finally finished securing the makeshift splint – a long, roughly hewn broom handle – huffed out a weary sigh of relief, and tried to straighten his aching back. He was so, so very tired. Tired of fighting to keep the child alive, of being so far from home, and most of all, tired of living among a bunch of warmongers.

A soft whimper drew his eyes back to her face.

She looked nothing like her usual pretty self. One eye had swollen shut and the skin had marbled into a purple and greenish yellow. The bruise spread across her high cheekbone, and down to her wide-set mouth with earnest, full lips. Kearn had trouble seeing the same child whose family he had been friends with for years. He reached out to smooth away the blood-encrusted black hair from her forehead. Sweat beaded on her skin, and he rested fingers against her brow to check for fever. Warm, but not dangerous. He could see her eyes moving beneath her lids. Her eyebrows occasionally knit. The corenroot was wearing off and he had no more to give her, so she would be in a great deal of pain very soon. Another thing to worry about.

He needed more light, and the fire was running low on logs. There hadn't been time to gather more, and the storm would have soaked anything he could have burned anyway. He looked around the one-room cabin, trying to spot any potential lamps that he might have missed in that first hurried search. Or the fourth, when he looked again despite knowing there was nothing he could use. Hopefully she would be stable enough to leave alone soon. He needed to hunt and gather food or they would both starve, but that would be hours spent away and he still worried about fever. They were getting low on his other provisions too. Between him keeping the wounds clean and the superior physiology that made him envy her Sano healing, infection hadn't set in yet. She still bled profusely from the deeper wounds when he changed the bandages, so she wasn't past danger yet.

With a frustrated groan, Kearn turned his attention to the young girl's feet. He checked to make sure he had enough bandages and started peeling the old yellow-and-red-soaked ones away. They were much better than the day before. Scabbing had covered most of the cuts.

The front door of the cabin flung open, slamming against the wooden wall, and Kearn flinched so hard that he found himself on his feet before he'd registered his own reaction. A woman stomped in and shook the heavy hood she wore, flinging water all over the floor.

Kearn's world narrowed in. 'Yarin?' he ventured, and the woman threw her hood back. He sighed in relief at the sight of her familiar short-cropped black hair and the ugly scar where her right ear should be. The roar of the rain pouring behind her drowned out the leaking droplets inside, and she met his gaze for a moment before looking around the old room. She reached back to take off the bulky pack she wore, and then turned and threw the door shut once more.

'Pulle told me where to go. I have some supplies,' she said without greeting. 'Medicine. Bandages. Food, too. How is she?'

Kearn stood to take the massive bag she held out. He wasn't expecting it to be as heavy as it was, and it momentarily unbalanced him.

'We were running low. She's still alive.'

Yarin took off the coat, dropped it to the floor with a wet thump, and stepped up to the bed. She pushed aside the swords hanging from her hip so the scabbards didn't obstruct her approach, and then knelt on the bed next to the young girl and pressed two fingers to her forehead. Kearn stepped up to the opposite side of the bed, just remembering to dodge the leak near the foot, and set down Yarin's bag so he could start going through it. Yarin bent in close and turned her head to feel the young girl's breath against her face, then dropped her head to rest gently against the girl's chest. Kearn looked away from the two Sano; something about their dark heads bent so close together felt intimate.

He took stock of the bag's contents as he waited for Yarin to finish her initial inspection. She casually lifted an arm to check the bandage, and the young girl flinched in her sleep.

Kearn's hand shot out in warning. 'Careful!' he snapped. 'Several of her limbs are broken. You'll cause more damage if you handle her like that.'

Yarin raised an eyebrow at him, and stepped back with a dismissive shrug. She snatched his stool from the end of the bed and moved it next to the girl's shoulder, straddled the rickety wooden thing, and crossed her arms with a frown.

'Pulle said she fell? How far did they chase her?'

'He found her at the bottom of a cliff,' Kearn said as he pulled a thick section of raw corenroot from the bag. He sagged a little in relief. 'They'd chased her maybe three leagues from the old fort. She didn't have shoes.'

Yarin's gaze dropped briefly to the girl's uncovered feet. Kearn thought he saw the ghost of a smile on her lips.

'She is her father's daughter,' she said. There was a hint of pride in her voice. Then she started looking around. 'Where is the sword?'

Kearn pointed to the main rafter, cutting through the center of the cabin above their heads. Yarin stepped up onto the stool and reached out to retrieve a long package wrapped in cloth and tied with a bloody rope. She ran a thumb across the brittle surface as her eyes travelled the length of it in thought.

'She had it when she fell. Pulle found it nearby,' Kearn explained when she looked up at him. 'Along with the body of the man who was chasing her.'

'Just one?' Yarin pulled away the rough material to look at the hilt of the sword within, and used a finger to peer down along the blade.

'Just one body. No one else in the area. There were a number of dead attackers at the fort. I suspect this was the last one left alive after they killed the Emperor. Pulle is out covering the trail. I haven't heard from him in three days.'

She nodded. 'He got word to me two days ago. I came as soon as I could.' She pulled out the sword and held it up before the hearth so distorted flames flickered through the glasslike blade. A deep green light fell onto her chest as the light refracted, and she tipped the sword to look down its sharply angled side. Not a single scratch anywhere on the weapon, Kearn noted, though he'd witnessed it in battle many times. There was no pommel, but the leather straps wrapped around the hilt creaked with Yarin's movement. It had been forged as one solid piece from handle to tip, and this was the first time Kearn had actually seen it this close.

'Definitely the Dragon's Claw,' Yarin said in an offhand tone and wrapped the sword back up to lay it on the bed. She looked down at the girl again, and neither she nor Kearn spoke again for a time. The steady drum of the rain lent a somber background to their thoughts, until Yarin turned to look at the various loud leaks in annoyance.

'You said the one chasing her was dead?' she asked.

Kearn bent to reach into his boot, and straightened back up with a small knife in hand which he waved around meaningfully. Yarin turned to look at it.

'He didn't die from the fall.'

Yarin's brows raised. 'She killed him? With that?'

Kearn nodded. He wondered which fact surprised her more. 'The last survivor of the raid to kill her father...'

'Making her...'

Kearn gave a small smile at the surprise in Yarin's eyes, which was soon matched by a smirk of her own. Then abruptly, Yarin's triumphant pleasure faded and her expression drew into dark thought. Heavy lines dug in between her brows, and she whirled away from the bed.

'All the more reason for them to look for her then. They'll be looking for the sword too.'

'It'll take months for her to heal, even as one of your kind,' Kearn said, anticipating her train of thought.

'Can'aan won't even care about her legitimacy. He will see to it that a new Emperor is named. Someone who doesn't challenge our people's ways. They just need the sword.'

'So it needs to go.'

She nodded. 'Yes. I'll take it with me now and hide it until she's ready.' She started pacing the cabin. Droplets of water splattered across her hauberk as she moved, but she walked through them without noticing. The sight made Kearn lean a little, as though he could direct her steps around the assaulting water. 'You will stay with her until she heals?'

Kearn nodded and lifted his hands to spin the clan ring around his right forefinger. 'As I said, it will take months.'

'Contact me when she is healed. I will keep her in my pride until the time is right.'

Kearn raised an eyebrow. 'Until the time is right for what?'

'For her to follow in her father's footsteps.' Yarin walked up to the bed to reach out for the sword.

Kearn intercepted her. 'It would be better for her to come with me,' he said. 'I want to return to my homeland and warn them. She just lost her whole family, and she'll just be hunted here whether or not she chooses to take up her father's legacy.'

Yarin abandoned her reach for the sword and straightened to step up toe to toe with him, every sinew projecting danger. Her direct gaze locked with his. 'That is not your choice, Fey,' she snapped.

'It's her choice,' Kearn said firmly, and inched closer to her so that they were staring each other down with equally hostile intensity. 'But it is one she will need to make when she is healed, and not some years later when you think she might be ready. I can take her back to Syridor and look after her. She will have a good life there.'

Yarin's jaw clenched, then relaxed. She broke away from their glare, conceding, and looked down at the girl.

'She is our future,' she said, her firm voice as raw as Kearn had ever heard it. 'I can't just let you take her away from us.'

'She is not the only avenue the rebels have to a new future, Yarin,' Kearn said. 'Anyone can step up and lead.'

'Yes, but she is Khamal's daughter,' Yarin said, and turned back to look him in the eye again. 'And she just claimed the throne by killing her father's killer. Can'aan will try to hide it and try to set up a false Emperor, but we will have the real one. And we have the sword. Those truths alone will call the Sano to our side, and we need every advantage we can get.'

Kearn hesitated. 'What if she doesn't want to?' he asked.

Yarin bent to reach for the sword and slapped away his hand when he tried to interfere again. She stood and tied the bloody rope to her belt.

'Send me word when she is healed,' she said, and walked over to scoop up her wet coat. She went to the door and pulled it open, then hesitated. She looked back at the bed.

'She had a family, which is more than what the rest of us ever knew,' Yarin said. 'The rest of her people deserve a chance to find out what that is like.'

Kearn shook his head. 'If the Sano deserve anything, it is to kill each other off in this inbred war of theirs. That man was more than his people ever deserved. He was... he was a good man. Something I would never accuse another Sano of being.'

Yarin glared at him. Kearn managed to keep his tone solid despite his grief, but his eyes were watering by the end of his little speech. He hoped that the firelight was too dim for her to see.

'This is war, Fey,' she said, and her voice was as sharp as her swords. 'We can't afford to be good, and she cannot go with you to your homeland. If I find out you have left with her, I will hunt you down myself.'

Kearn didn't respond. 'She will need a new name until the time is right to reveal who she is,' Yarin said. 'Cut her hair and call her Ahela.'

Then the door slammed shut once more, and Yarin was gone. Kearn turned back to his patient and looked down at her ravaged feet. He didn't know whether her wounds were a testament to how terrified she'd been, or how determined. Either way, she'd run for leagues after her family had been butchered, and then managed to kill the man who hunted her. Kearn wasn't sure how she'd fallen off the cliff. Maybe it had been mutual destruction. Maybe it was just that, after fighting so long for survival, she'd just been too exhausted to keep going. He could only speculate, but whatever the reason, she was alive and fighting for her life after a fall that should have killed her.

Regardless of who she was, she was brave, and strong. A fighter. 'Ahela.'

Hyacinth

Daniel Dicks

The wind whispered 'Change'. As I was with you,
And we sat watching the shadows bloom; strange,
Dark flowers in evening's light, bruising-blue,
The wind whispered 'Change'.

Trees and their leaves prematurely estranged
Tainting the path, the park, the avenue,
Scattered in that voice's echoing range

A warning, of something just out of view.
I couldn't have known, what I would exchange,
What I would sacrifice, for loving you.
The wind whispered 'Change'.

Dolce Far Niente

Daniel Dicks

Not to mimic your warmth
The feeling of being in your arms
Or burying my head in your neck,
I bring the covers up close
Almost to my eyes,
Careful not to block the light
Soft and grey
As it falls perhaps like water
From between the gap in the curtains

And not because I miss your voice
The soft white noise
Of your tired breaths,
I leave the record playing out
Till the melody turns to static
And then to silence

Though I suppose I do
Miss you. But that's ok, I think, and anyway,
There's nothing I can do about that now,
So I let my eyes grow heavy,
And memories give way to dreams

The House

Sarah O'Hara

In September, the families started moving in. We watched the road changing in increments. Cars appeared, parked very carefully by people unaccustomed to reversing up steep driveways. Children played on squeaking trampolines. Ornamental rockeries could be glimpsed in long gardens. People drifted around the top floors of the newly built houses, lit up in the wide glass windows, restlessly looking out. Above the houses, the sky opened up – blue unfolding on blue, the aching height of it pressing down on their slate roofs, cool and shaded beneath the jagged brow of the fells. But the biggest house remained empty and still looked unfinished. The building work had been disrupted, naturally. As long as we were watching it, nobody moved in. The 'For Sale' sign seemed to take root in the earth, solid and reassuring. Can you feel sorry for a house? We did – for the future it had lost and for the family that would one day live in it. We pitied these offcomers, who would surely feel uneasy on the staircase or in the basement and shrug it off, perhaps without ever understanding why.

Autumn stayed warm. On the fells, dead bracken and sheep's wool steamed brown and grey, and every evening our village smelt of woodsmoke and barbecues. We ate blackened burgers with ketchup smeared on white bread, and our mothers pulled up fresh mint from their gardens and tore it, still earth-flecked, over tinned peaches. The last of the berries were now gone from the bushes.

The weather was still dry and sunny when our year went back to school, two weeks later than everyone else. The rest of the school eyeballed us in the corridors. We were back to six-thirty starts, our mothers making packed lunches whilst younger siblings spilt sweet cereal-milk down their pyjamas, and outside the early mornings rumbled into life: milk bottles set down, clinking on porches, passing cars whooshing by, newspapers landing *thwack* on front steps. Our bus wound past farmhouses to school on the other side of the valley, an old abbey surrounded by thick, black pine forests. The bells were back, as were the weeds in the netball court; the boarded-up well where rainwater collected; the round apples swelling on trees turning copper and gold, trees that long-dead nuns had once nurtured. Despite the still-warm weather, the birds changed too. With the influx of new pupils, the summer songbirds melted away, as swallows gave way to languid stretches of ducks and swans coming home south across the mountains, and we went back to school without her, without Grace.

I noticed the new girl before everyone else did. At lunch on the first day back, I slipped away from the canteen and went out to the playground. She was at the school gates, standing between two worried parents who were talking to our headteacher. While they chatted, she watched blackbirds settle on the cover of the well. When horses wandered up to the playground she stepped back in surprise, so I knew that she had come from a city. Later that day, I saw her standing in the corridor with a map on a napkin that one of the office ladies had probably given to her. There was a lost look in her eyes, a hesitancy as she shifted from one foot to another, one that felt horribly familiar, and I almost – *almost* – offered to help.

She seemed okay at first. She was shy, embarrassed of the mismatched uniform that marks out a new kid: navy socks instead of grey, a cardigan instead of a v-necked jumper. But then she told someone that her family was renting a house in town before their new one was finished.

'My mum's not happy with it,' she said. 'We're getting a new staircase.'

After school that day, we skipped the bus and went back to the house, walking that same old route for the first time since it happened. No one had walked that way since before the summer, and maybe it was just my new school shoes, but my feet felt heavy, moved slowly. When we got to the house, the 'For Sale' sign was gone.

The road was built into an old quarry, moving round in a steep circle, with the biggest house in the centre on its own modest hill. The new houses were all wood and glass and slate, and their gardens were not pristine lawns but slopes of rocky ground and trees. From the road, you couldn't see much of the biggest house, just a steep driveway leading to a ring of pine trees encircling it at the top. But we all agreed that day, when we got there on our bicycles and craned our heads up at where the sign had been, it felt different. Perhaps the trees had been tidied up; we spotted circles of pine needles and dead leaves that had been swept across the driveway. A van idled at the bottom of the road, belonging to an electrician or a gardener, or perhaps a carpenter, someone to fix the stairs. The house, for too long vacant and incomplete, was almost finished now, was nearly made whole.

Back at school, I'm not sure whose idea it was to ignore the new girl. I don't think it was mine, but no one else owned up to it either. I guess it was just bad luck for her that she happened to be in our year.

That first week she kept on smiling nervously at lunch as she sat down next to us. In lessons she offered her pencils or rulers if someone had forgotten theirs. She didn't volunteer answers when our teacher asked, even though I saw how quickly she wrote in her exercise book, and I wondered if she had moved often, if she was used to this new-girl thing. I hoped that they were one of those families who moved every six months or year, and yet every day plasterers and painters and tree surgeons spilled in and out of that house on the hill, smoothing off its sharp new edges, making it ready, making it theirs.

Her face began to fall when we shifted along the table at lunchtimes, taking care to place one of our book bags on an empty seat next to us; when we doubled back at the end of school so that she walked out of the gates alone. At break-time we made up elaborate, convoluted games that no one could join unless we told them the rules, which we wrote down on pink paper and passed around in front of her, whispering loudly to each other, *sign your name here if you want to play.*

'Oh, you still play games,' she said, to no-one in particular. 'At my old school everyone just chatted.'

If anyone else heard her say that, they all ignored it too.

At lunch she wandered along the playground's edge and watched the distant horses. In lessons, she seemed to now be doodling instead of writing. I think some of the older girls felt sorry for her, and decided to sit next to her at lunchtime, giving her the Lucozades and chocolate buttons they could buy from the senior tuck-shop. They didn't tell us off, though. They couldn't blame us.

The warmth and the blueness drained out of the sky, and for most days in October a thin rain worked itself into the fells. We went to see the house most weekends, watching them finish it, watching its airy structure take root in the ground. The various workmen had been replaced with furniture vans, filled with an endless parade of rolled-up rugs and armchairs and even a piano. Sometimes I thought

I could see the new girl looking at us through the trees. Around then we started to argue with each other, about whether or not it was fair to shut her out like that. We also argued about Grace.

No one could remember who was the last one of us to see her. We debated whether she was wearing jeans or dungarees; the dungarees were her favourite but, as someone pointed out, maybe that meant she would be less likely to wear them on a quiet country walk in the evening. We all knew she was last seen by the trees on the edge of the village, out towards the old quarry, but we couldn't decide which direction she walked in. As we were discussing this I snapped and said, 'What does it matter which direction she walked in? We all know where she ended up.'

The others were all silent after that, pawing uselessly at the pedals of their bikes, and I cycled off first so that the wind could cool my hot, stinging eyes before they noticed them.

On our way to the house, we passed by the straggling thicket of trees that was not quite a wood. The road, leading eventually to our school, was always quiet in the summer holidays. She had walked alone, then. And if I hadn't said to her that I was bored of just walking around the same places, that I didn't want to go near school in the holidays, well, it was a walk she had done alone a hundred times before. We all had. And the road would have always been in sight if Grace had paused here, head half-turned, her blue jeans or dungarees standing out against the grey rocks and the trees, a bit muddied and crumpled at the hem. Like one of the deer that sometimes wandered over from the forest, half-glimpsed from the roadside with its head turned: a flash of brown and white spots and skittish hoofs that sent cloudy water flying across the tarmac.

I was alone when I next saw the new girl. She was standing at the top of her driveway surrounded by the rocky walls of the quarry, wearing a thin t-shirt despite the rain. Behind her, the house was lit up in a bright patchwork of windows. When she saw me she stared, and I stared back. After a while, she raised her hand. I cycled off quickly up the road.

Not long after that someone told on us, and our mothers all gave us individual lectures for spying, bullying, intimidation, and cruelty. They rattled the words off, raising a finger for each one, saying, *leave those poor people alone, or else.* So we stopped going to the house, cycling past the trees, pausing against the walls of the old quarry and looking up into its windows. But it seemed too late to be friends with her now. She had stopped trying, anyway. She often went home from school early with stomach-aches, or arrived late after break-time, claiming she'd had a dentist appointment, or doctor's appointment, and then eventually just appearing midway through a lesson with no excuse for the teacher.

One morning in November our school flooded, and we had to stay at home for the day. Our mothers wouldn't let us go out into the rain that was now beating into the fells, turning the mud red and blue with fresh dye off the sheep's backs. But I managed to slip out while mine was on a phone call. I had heard her talking to our neighbour about the flooding, saying it was apparently worse at the edge of the village, where the roads were steep. The weather was too bad for my bike, so I put on my wellies and walked out to the old quarry.

I paused at the top of the road. Around me, the houses stood like sleek grey islands as rain bounced off them. Black groundwater was running down from the big house along its steep driveway, towards a Mercedes. A thin, youngish woman in a beige tracksuit stood at the bottom of the driveway, staring at her stuck car in horror, leaves and mud gummed up around its wheels. The new girl looked out from the top of the driveway, sheltered by trees. Our eyes met. This time, I raised my hand first.

The woman in the tracksuit was on her phone when I reached the driveway. She sensed me walking up behind her and turned around, her face panicked.

'Do you live around here?' she said. 'Can you help? The water's rising through the floor. The foundations – I don't know why – our basement's already flooded and it's still rising.'

The bottom half of her tracksuit was coated in mud. Her hair was an expensive brown shade that reminded me of mahogany and stillness. It hung around her shoulders in damp tangles.

'Can you help?' the woman said again. 'I can't get through to the builders.'

'My mum uses sandbags,' I said eventually. 'Do you have any?'

'We didn't think we needed any.' Her expression was defiant. 'It's on a hill. That's why we wanted it. We were told any flooding wouldn't reach us.'

'Do you have soil for your garden? You could put that in bin-bags.'

'You'll help me, won't you?' She took my elbow and turned me towards the house with a surprising amount of strength. 'There's bags and bags of soil. I'm going to level the garden out, put a proper lawn down and a flower patch, and clear out those rocks and some of the trees that block out all our light.'

She continued to chatter as she steered me up the driveway, slowly, because she was trying to avoid the running water. I didn't look at the house, but I felt it looking at me, solemn and spacious and thick-walled, the wood and slate casting shadows across my face.

The new girl had retreated to the shelter of their front porch. She shivered and frowned at me.

'Darling, this nice girl is going to help us stop the flooding,' the woman said brightly. I couldn't help turning away from them, gazing up at the house and into its rain-sheeted windows like a moth to a flame. When I was looking away she added in a loud whisper, 'Ask if she's from your school, yeah? You could make friends!'

When I looked back at them the woman had already gone inside. I could hear her voice in the long, dim hallway saying that it was lucky she'd kept the soil on top of the lawnmower so it was still dry. The new girl watched me warily.

'Hi,' I said.

There was a pause and the new girl glanced behind her, into the dark centre of the house, as if longing to follow her mother in there and close the door, to shut me out. Around us, clay dislodged itself from the quarry walls with loud cracks.

'I didn't ask to live here,' she said eventually. 'I'm not trying to upset anybody.'

Before I could reply she turned and followed her mother into the house.

I felt sorry for them then, as I peered into the hallway, where there was a new glass staircase clinging to the wall. I tried to see it as they saw it, when the radio was on and the windows were open and the new girl laughed and played in the sheltered trees. When the sun streaked the freshly-painted walls with golden light as it set over the mountains, over the quarry, over a complete house and a full family and a life allowed to resume. But it was no good. They knew what had happened, but they would never really know. Not the way we knew, how it had been.

It is a scene we all know. It hangs before us at night-time, when the wind creaks, when our parents are quiet downstairs and it feels like we are alone. The empty house, just built, glowing with a new and sunken pallor. Through bare windows a complimentary television waits in the darkness, silent and shrouded. Glossy open-house brochures shine on the new solid-wood floors. She was last seen at dusk, but I picture her there in the moonlight. He lurks in the shadows of the quiet, empty rooms, as she is laid out by the staircase like an offering. No newspaper article could make them know as we know it, as we have constantly imagined it – Grace's last journey from the trees by the road up here to the house on the hill, unseen, unused, and waiting.

The door stood ajar. Inside, the new girl helped her mother carry a sandbag down into the basement. I stepped into the house.

Looking Back at You

Maria Henry

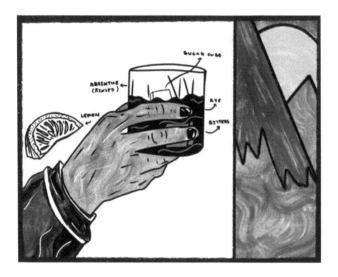

It was an ordinary Wednesday night in 1965, business was slow and only a few regulars lurked around in the corners, sipping their usual drinks and sitting in their usual seats – just far enough away from each other that they didn't have to talk to one another, yet close enough so that they didn't feel alone. I was growing increasingly bored of serving the same pints of beer to the same boring people – too set in their ways to try anything more exciting than the *oh so classic*

'whiskey on the rocks'. That's when a man I didn't recognise sat down in front of me. He ordered a Sazerac: rye, bitters, absinthe (rinsed), sugar cube, lemon peel; on the rocks. *Finally*, I thought, *someone interesting.*

The mysterious man was clearly not from around these parts and attracted an array of stares from the locals who wore denim jeans and leather jackets every single night as though the fate of their world depended on it. He wore a white tasselled suit and flared Stetson hat with a gold trim over his head of long greying hair. His feet were covered by pointed ivory boots that were scuffed around the heels; his hands were concealed by white velvet gloves and around his neck, bringing the whole eclectic look together, he wore a gold bolo tie.

He was around the age of sixty, from what I could deduce from the deep lines on his face, the thin skin under his eyes, and the cracking of his voice as he placed his order; he was probably a smoker, *definitely a drinker*. In front of him he placed a folder full of disorganised papers, tied up messily with a green elastic band. He kept one hand on it at all times, as if it contained all the unknown secrets of the universe.

He was quiet at first, tapping his gloved fingers along the folder, drawing my attention towards it. *Sure, I'll bite.*

'Whatcha got there, a school project?' I asked.

He gave me a glare that implied I shouldn't pry further, *or maybe he just got scared*. I decided it was best to leave it alone, at least for now. We engaged in some polite small-talk; chatted about the weather – *cold, too cold, quite unpleasant* – and the war in Vietnam – *terrible, escalating far too quickly, but what did we expect with a man like Johnson running the roost?* – but my mind kept wandering back to what was in that folder. When he was nearly finished with his cocktail, the overproof rye warming his cheeks rose-red, I decided to try again; maybe this time he'd open up to me. Our eyes met as he caught me glancing at the folder once more.

'What's in this folder is a story,' he said. 'I can tell you, but you're not going to believe it. No one ever does.'

'How about another one on the house?' I asked him as I reached for the rye. I was bored of repeating the same actions: wiping down the bar, waiting for someone new to come in, polishing the glasses, restocking shelves. I wanted to keep him for a little longer, he'd piqued my interest.

'Well, if you insist,' he replied, feigning humility, pretending to be holding back when I could tell he'd been waiting for the chance to get into it.

'It was 1930, a crystal-clear night in October...' He took another big swig of his Sazerac, eyeing the jigger as I filled it with more for his next.

'It's good,' he flicked his eyes up to meet mine – *nobody around here ever does that*. 'Hard-pressed to find a bartender true to the craft in these parts. Anyways... It was one of those endless summer nights, where the air is warm but not too sticky and the moon is bright and silvery in the sky. I went to meet my girlfriend; she wanted to go look at the stars. She snuck out of the window of her parents house to join me – clambered all the way down to the roof of the porch, and then shimmied herself down the trunk of an oak tree to the ground. When I asked her how she planned to get back in she said she'd "figure it out" and that it didn't matter half as much as the getting out did.'

He smiled. 'The way she looked at me, the lil' specks of gold in her brown eyes, I'll never forget that. I remember thinking I would marry this woman one day – maybe one day real soon if she'd give me the chance.'

He beamed when he spoke about her, his eyes glowed with a passion I didn't often see in the regulars that came in here – all dull eyed and dazed. *This was a man still in love.*

'What's her name?' I asked.

'Nancy,' he replied. 'Her name was – *is* – Nancy… and for a while, we were the two happiest people in the whole world. Then something happened and everything was thrown off. It all turned to chaos. This part is hard to explain…'

He polished off his cocktail as I poured another standard-order-beer for one of the regulars. He tapped the bar indicating he was ready for his next. I continued preparing it and he watched my hands closely, as though he knew the process and was waiting to see if I got it right. *I always do.* I rinsed the absinthe into a fresh glass and strained the rest of the Sazerac in, with ice on the side. *That ought to keep him talking.*

With a little more liquid-courage, he jumped back into it, '—I was looking at Nancy, I wanted to ask her something important – *the big question*, you know?'

I nodded.

'I was trying to muster the courage to get the words out all night, searching for some kind of poetry nonsense to prove to her how special she was. But, as I opened my mouth to speak, we were struck by an immense white light, so bright it blinded us to anything else in the park. I tried to speak but I found my mouth wouldn't open. It was like a void opening up and swallowing us whole with a velocity unlike anything I'd ever known. Gravity failed as it took us higher, light becoming an endless prism, like being sucked into a mammoth kaleidoscope.'

He fixed his gaze on me once more, his eyes were wild and his hands were tensely clenched around his glass.

'So, what happened to you?' I asked, becoming increasingly invested, but half keeping an eye on what looked like the beginning of a squabble breaking out across the bar. He looked up to me, capturing my full attention with his gaze, took a deep breath and continued.

'When I woke up I found myself in some sort of machine. The blinding white started to fade out to grey and I could see various smaller lights appearing in the distance, flaring up in pink-ish blinks around the room. Apart from that, it was all grey – a large grey circle made of… of something like metal, but I'll get to that. The perimeters of the room were as dark as the night sky itself. I tried to move towards the edge, but something held me back. I tried to call out to Nancy, but my voice didn't make a sound, all the usual vibrations without the usual reverberations. My feet made no noise against the floor and although it was metallic, no reflection appeared upon its surface.'

I placed the fresh drink in front of him. Hee dumped the ice in immediately and took a large gulp. Then looked up to me with these big wide eyes like a child looking at a parent they idolise – he wanted so badly for me to believe him. It was *pretty damn crazy*, but there was something in his desperation, in his I-should-not-be-telling-you-this-but-I-need-to demeanour, that made me want to.

'It was alive,' he continued.

'I don't know how to explain this to you but the machine itself was alive. It was breathing around me, taking all my energy until I fell to the ground unconscious. I woke up, who knows how long later, and the darkness that surrounded the room was gone, revealing large metal walls, the same as the floor. I studied them, looking for an escape, only to find that there was none – the walls were perfectly smooth with not a single crack or scratch showing. I stood up, cautiously, and walked around the room – then I reached out a finger to touch it. The wall moved beneath my hand; as though malleable like dough. But it didn't *feel like anything*, in that, it had no real consistency or texture, it just sort of *moved*. Nothing in the machine *felt* like anything, never hot nor cold, never any sound – just an intangible sort of space in which nothing really happened, and nothing really existed.

'I worried about Nancy, about where she might be and if she'd met the same fate as me. Or I thought maybe I'd died, and this was some variation of an afterlife, some waiting room for Heaven or a first step into Hell. I closed my eyes, feeling tired like I'd never felt before, and I fell into a deep sleep. When I woke some time later the first sight I saw was that of my hands. I was missing a finger. All that remained in the space of my index was a bare patch of skin, not a single stitch or wound. It was almost like it had never existed on my hand at all.'

He removed his velvet glove to reveal a pale, wrinkled hand. It was true that his finger was missing. I looked closely at it and I found that there was not a scratch nor scar that showed any evidence of its removal. *Strange – maybe he was born without a finger? Yes. That must be it. That's the only explanation.*

He quickly put the glove back on. I gave him more ice for his drink.

'But that's not even the strangest part,' he said. 'The part that really got me, is that when I looked down at my hands, I found they were different. Not only was my finger gone, but they were aged, wrinkled slightly around the edges and across the knuckles. I then looked down at the rest of my body, I felt my face – it was the same, it was mine, but it was older, my skin was softer, thinner under the eyes and with lines ridging my forehead. I had a beard where hair had never properly grown before. I wanted to scream, I tried to, but it evaporated into the void, floating away from me. How long had I been asleep? Had it been years?'

He asked me these questions like he expected an answer, like he was desperately searching for any possibility of one. *What could I say to a man so crazed?*

'Now, you better pour yourself something and sit down because here comes the weirdest part,' he continued, anxiously tapping his fingers against his glass. No one else had come in, so I poured myself a Fernet-Branca neat, crossed my arms and leaned in to hear the rest of his tale.

'The next time I woke up, I felt something beneath me – the numbness was gone. I ran my hands along the ground and I could feel grass and dirt building up beneath my nails. I could *feel* it.'

He really did sound insane.

'Where were ya?' I asked.

'Back where I started,' he replied, 'it was the same field I'd been taken from that night when it happened. Only now there were fewer trees, the grass was a little browner, and the houses that surrounded it looked taller than I remembered. For a while I just lay there, feeling the ground, breathing the air, looking up at the stars for answers. Then I slowly got up, wobbling like a fawn learning to walk for the first time. Nobody else was around. I stumbled towards the houses – their windows with their little yellow lights guided me down the block. The streets were familiar to me, I remembered my way home. Everything looked bigger, the cars were bigger and there were more of them, two in nearly every driveway, and the houses seemed to be more squashed together as if a bunch of them had popped up overnight and filled in the gaps. When I reached my own house, I walked in as I would any other day; my mother always left the door unlocked. This is when I caught a glimpse of myself in the glassy window of the porch door, the first time I'd seen myself since I was taken – I looked like my father had looked the last time I saw him. On the table there was a newspaper dated Wednesday, October 15, 1960.'

'How's that even poss—'

He cut me off before I could get the words out.

'I don't know. I don't know how it happened, but it seemed that thirty-something years had passed since I'd been taken onto that machine or ship or whatever it was. What had felt like a "nothing" amount of time for me, had actually been a good half of a lifetime for everybody else.'

He took his hand off the ominously-guarded folder and shifted it over to me.

'What is it?' I asked. The long-awaited secret unfolding before me, the suspense had made me feel as though I was on the cusp of discovering something life-changing and intrigue was quickly consuming me

'*Research*,' he replied. I opened it up eagerly to find drawings, scribbles, pages upon pages of notes and newspaper cut-outs, the one on the top was dated 1963 and the headline read: 'TIME TRAVEL: NASA EXECUTIVE ASKS "WHEN WILL IT BE POSSIBLE?"'

'The lights were still on in the living room. I peered around the corner, trying to avoid making any noise.'

'And what'd ya find?' I asked, sipping on my Fernet, flicking through his manic collection of artifacts, trying to make sense of them all.

'They weren't my parents, just some other family I didn't know – a man, a woman, both around my age – or, *my new age* – and two little kids were sitting on the floor in front of the television. The furniture was all changed too, I figured somebody else had bought the house – but then the woman stood up to draw the blinds and I saw her face illuminated by the amber glow of the streetlamp. *It was Nancy.* I was about to run up to her but then I looked around the room and saw all the photos that used to be of me and my parents. They were now of Nancy; Nancy at all ages, Nancy at her wedding, Nancy with her children.'

'Well, what'd you do? Did ya talk to her?' I asked, somewhat more eagerly than I wanted to let on.

'*What could I do?*' he replied. 'Whatever had happened to me, hadn't happened to her – she'd lived thirty years without me. She'd made a life for herself. I was a stranger to her now. I didn't know who I was, or *what* I was. Or, if it was even real, if I could trust her, if I could trust me – if I could trust anything ever again. *Hell,* I don't even know if this is real or if I'm still up on that thing hallucinating. Maybe my life is all just some big glitch in the universe.'

'I can assure you this is real,' I laughed, touching my arm to prove I wasn't a hologram, '*see*, real as they come.'

'That's exactly what you would say if you weren't real,' he replied. And, I must admit, he was probably right. The strangest part of it all was that he was the 'realest' person I'd met in a long time. *Crazy* for sure, but real nevertheless.

He seemed to exist independently from the usual beer-chugging, denim-wearing crowd. He looked me in the eyes when he told me his stories – he reminded me that life exists beyond this wooden bar.

He pushed the empty glass towards me, signalling that he was done for the night. I almost felt a jolt of sadness. I gave him back his folder, left open on a page titled: 'ALIEN ABDUCTION: HOW DO YOU KNOW IF IT'S HAPPENED TO YOU?'

'So, where'd you go next?' I asked, clearing the glass away.

'Oh, *here, there, and everywhere*,' he replied with a half-laugh-half-sigh, 'I've spent the last four years trying to figure out what the hell happened that night, what happened in those thirty years I missed, and all I've found is more mystery and more misery.' His eyes shifted back to the open folder. He began to gather the papers.

I looked at him, leaned over the bar a little, and because I couldn't help myself from wondering, asked him, 'You really think there's aliens out there doin' these things?'

'You don't have to believe me,' he said, looking me right in the eyes. 'But the next time you look up at the stars, don't tell me you don't feel like there's something looking back at you.'

He slid over a fifty-dollar bill, gave me a slight nod, implying *keep the change*, picked up his folder, and walked off into the night, letting the door swing behind him.

I walked out to my truck after locking up. It was around two in the morning, the sky was clear as they come, and the stars were twinkling out in full force. I looked up at them for a moment and thought about what the man had said. *Something looking back at ya.* Just as I was about to drive off, I thought I saw something flash up in pink. A shooting star, maybe? Or, *a glitch in the universe* perhaps. Then again, maybe I was just seeing things – it was that time of night when all sense seems to melt away, and everything is a little off until you wake up in the morning and reality starts up again.

Anduze

Sarah Hopkins

Sasha watched on silently as the wasp bounced off her skin, once, twice, then came to a stop on her leg, just below her knee. It settled, basking in the thin layer of sweat and sun lotion that veiled her. She wondered what had attracted the wasp to her; was it the warmth she was emitting, or the chemical coconutty scent of the tan enhancer she had sprayed liberally across herself moments before? It seemed too dazed, too relaxed to sting. Either way the threat remained.

'Like attracts like,' she muttered.

She lay back on the lounger, a bead of sweat tickling its way from her underarm down and round the gentle slope of her back, pooling somewhere beneath her. Yasmine drifted past on the cactus floatie that Jade had bought for nine euros at the market the day before.

'Ok. Six down. Three words, five, two, five. The clue is: "A debt to collect with a heavy heart; sterling only, Please." What the actual fuck?' Yasmine lowered her sunglasses so the group could see her eyes narrow.

Claudia was wading in the shallow end of the pool. 'Does anything start with a capital?'

'Yes, the "Please."'

'Ok, then I think that means that one of the words starts with P.'

'It's Pound of Flesh.' Sasha was still watching the wasp on her shin. It looked as though it had fallen asleep. Or died. She envied it either way.

Yasmine counted the squares, trying not to let the surprise show on her face that Sasha had even been listening. Sasha, who in previous years had commandeered both floaties and pool-side activities, had been silent all day. All week, in fact.

'That fits.'

'How the *heck* did you get that?' Erin, on the lounger next to Sasha, shifted onto
her side. She shielded her eyes against the sun, but they were still screwed up in disbelief.

Sasha brushed the wasp off her. It rose, reluctantly, its wings sputtering to life, then landed once more on the lounger, between her legs. Not wishing to disturb it further, she stood carefully, then looked down at Erin, her lips curled up at the corners in a half-smile.

'Sterling is pound, heavy heart is the flesh – and something you'd die without. *Merchant of Venice* is a pretty messed up play. It resonates.' She bent and picked up her book, *Bearing the Unbearable*. Claudia had lent it to her at the start of the holiday, but it wasn't really the poolside thriller she'd been craving. 'Probably because I think about revenge a lot.'

She wasn't looking at the group, yet she felt the air around her stagnate, a stillness settling amongst them as their gazes bounced warily between each other and her. She tucked the book under her arm. 'I'm heading in for a bit. Anyone want anything from the house?'

She was met with silence.

On her way inside, Sasha scanned the edges of the garden, searching for the small black body of the scorpion. It was definitely dead, yet she maintained a small flicker of hope that it had somehow revived itself, had scuttled back to its spiky friends and was recounting its treacherous tale.

They cleared the pool each morning, choosing to do the job themselves as opposed to letting the staring pool men back. That morning, floating close to the surface at the deep end, was the scorpion. It had long since succumbed to the gentle lapping of the chlorinated waves, but even in death it secreted a potent danger. When Sasha scooped it out using the net, the other girls made her walk to the very edge of the wooded garden to shake it loose. It was the first time any of them had seen a scorpion before, and they all gathered around the pool to watch Sasha complete her already-failed rescue mission. Claudia pulled out her phone, wanting to document the end of its earthside journey but Erin quickly rested her hand on Claudia's arm.

'Not everything needs to be filmed, Clauds,' she said, almost inaudibly. Claudia quickly put her phone away.

Each day started and ended the same. The girls would wake in stages, between seven and nine. Sasha was always awake first, having never really gone to sleep, and as the others stirred she would brew some coarse, black coffee on the stove, the first of many. The kitchen was the darkest room in the house; one small deep-set window with a foggy sheet of glass between them and the driveway. It was tiled, wall and ceiling, in terracotta. The tiles were so cold that in the mornings, they would alternate between their bare feet, balancing one on top of the other to keep the contact with the unwelcome chill to a minimum. By around midday they would seek solace amongst the tiles, sometimes lying face down on them, chests bared to sooth the prickly sting of a freshly-developed sunburn.

Erin would wander in next, her eyes still clouded from recently departed dreams. Sasha would hand her a mug of coffee, which Erin would drop two ice cubes into and a drizzle of rice milk.

Jade was always third to arrive, yet surprised each day that she wasn't first. She would brew a separate pot, decaffeinated, and stand with her arms around Sasha's waist, head rested on the bony protrusions of Sasha's shoulder, and they would watch it simmer gently together.

'Did you sleep?' She would ask, her voice muffled and warm.

'A bit.'

Depending on the amount of wine consumed the night before, Claudia would either stick her head through the small arch of the kitchen doorway, drink three gulps from the closest mug, then head out on her morning run. Or, as was more often the case, she'd trickle into the now cramped room and would open the fridge.

'Too early for a beer?' she would say, turning and grinning wolfishly at the room, shoving a handful of the previous night's dinner into her mouth.

They would wander down to the pool together, except for Yasmine, who would emerge from the house about half an hour after the pool netting was done.

'My dudes,' she would shout, from the top of the small stone steps leading from the side of the house to the garden, her booming voice at complete odds with the still setting of the French countryside. Smiling, she would reach her arms over her head and release a satisfied groan, hug the air, then bound through the archway of lavender and honeysuckle that separated the main garden from the pool. Moving between each of them, she would kiss them on any available part of their greasy skin, then wriggle her way into the best tanning spot, hushing over the moans of dismay with soothing coos of 'just shimmy up a bit that way.'

'Did any of my Pisceans have a dream last night that they absolutely *must* share? No? Then,' she would press the ON button for her portable speaker, the bleep-bloop search for a Bluetooth connection signalling that the day had truly begun, 'we're going back to the nineties, baby!'

At this point, Claudia would surreptitiously remove her hearing aids, giving a sly wink to anyone watching, and would dive all sleek and dolphin-like into the pool. And then they would lounge poolside – smoking cigarettes, bickering over crosswords, swapping coffee for beer then beer for rosé – for the majority of the day.

Every other day, two of the girls would drive the rented Fiat Panda down to the Intermarché on the outskirts of the next town. They would fill the boot with flimsy bottles of water and tubs of lemon sorbet that would melt before they'd make it back to the house. The others would greet them upon their return like wives waiting for their war-torn husbands, with the slight adjustment of being partially or entirely nude.

They would tear into their spoils, the scrambling only slowing for a moment as they passed around a jar of cornichons and dug awkwardly with index finger and thumb into the vinegary brine. Then lope, full and satiated, back to the pool.

Claudia and Yasmine had, to the bemusement of the others, 'discovered' Anduze almost seven years ago. After some trial and error, including a few tumultuous summers where Claudia had invited virtual strangers on the trip, the group had finally been curated, perfectly in Yasmine's opinion, and the five of them had returned every summer since. It was, they all agreed breathily most evenings, the best two weeks of the year. And each year was better than the last. Until, perhaps, this one.

On this particular trip, Sasha would retreat from the pool to the house at around two, hoping the cool breeze of the afternoon and her wine-dampened senses would allow her to nap, at least until the early evening. She was rarely successful, but she also knew the girls needed a few hours to themselves each afternoon to discuss that night's intervention. Idly imagining their hushed worrying pained Sasha, mostly, yet glimmering just out of sight in a corner of her mind, was a shard of contentedness. Each evening they would reconvene in the kitchen, eat together, then play cards and listen to music, or reenact scenes from previous summers. Apart from Sasha, who would clear the table, but then slink away to the front of the house at the first opportunity. She would lie on the gravel of the driveway, staring up at the stars.

'What are you doing?' Yasmine had asked, on their first night.

Sasha's head lolled lazily towards her. 'Looking for the silver lining.'

'That could be the worst fucking thing you've ever said.'

Sasha's eyes flicked back to the sky. 'Yeah. Maybe.'

Now, they watched on as Sasha made her way back to the house. She was wearing a ridiculous, childlike swimsuit, aqua blue and covered in cartoon fish. The group mercilessly teased her about it but each year, as almost a gift to them, Sasha had donned it at some point, occasionally with the accompaniment of a fluorescent snorkel or comically undersized goggles. They all agreed that their favourite combination was last summer when, somehow, Sasha had managed to find matching inflatable armbands, refusing to take them off all holiday. Despite the rings of white that had circled her arms due to their lack of sun exposure, the uncontrollable laughter of her friends was simply too good to give up. This year, however, the swimsuit seemed to hang lamely from her body, all humour rinsed from it.

When the front door had closed, Claudia turned to the group. 'I spoke to my old Criminal Justice professor today.' Claudia had passed the bar earlier in the summer but had spent the first ten weeks of The Ordeal, as they had since titled it, at The Center of Excellence in California, completing an intensive Arabic course. With a strict 'no technology on campus' rule, she had only learned of what had happened to Sasha after leaving, and had been plagued by an immense guilt in the months that had followed. At least now she could say 'I am a terrible friend' in Arabic.

'There's nothing that can be done, legally, unless she presses charges. I just wish I could turn back time.'

'Claudia,' Yasmine said, firmly. Yasmine had been the collector of the friends, finding them in various times and places throughout her life. Sasha, for instance, had first caught Yasmine's eye almost ten years ago in the smoking area of a nightclub in North London. With a cigarette dangling from one hand, and the other wrapped around the stem of a wine glass, Yasmine listened in as Sasha argued convincingly and passionately with a man in a business suit about the merits of reality television. In the years that had passed since, if anybody ever asked Yasmine if she believed in love at first sight she'd reference that first encounter with Sasha.

Yasmine had introduced the group to one another and had watched on, hawk-like and eager, as they had all fallen in love too. As she knew they would. But Claudia was the first, and maybe her favourite. 'None of this is anyone's fault. Apart from his.'

Jade tried with fumbling fingers to roll a cigarette. Yasmine took the paper from her hands, rolling the tobacco in a quick flourish.

'I don't understand why she won't press charges. Is she just going to spend the rest of her life reporting it on the sites that re-upload it? It's obviously him.'

Yasmine licked the edge of the cigarette paper and folded it down neatly, stuck the filtered tip of it in her mouth, and lit the other end. Taking a quick drag, she passed the cigarette back. 'She told me she didn't see the point in ruining two lives.' There was a brief pause. Yasmine simply shrugged.

'I thought that she didn't think there was enough evidence?'

'As if. The titles are pretty telling. I saw it the other day under "MILF's steamy affair *leaked*". What do people think "leaked" means?'

'Don't you have to have a child to qualify as a MILF?'

'Did you report it?'

'Obviously.'

They had each spent nearly every private moment since the first upload trawling sites, typing in progressively obscene descriptors into the search bars. But it seemed every time they came across the video and requested for it to be removed, three more uploads would appear in its place.

'It's like trying to fight a ghost,' Yasmine had said, back when they were in the trying-to-see-the-funny-side phase. When they were still calling it Sasha Superstar, thinking that it could maybe be laughed off, reported, deleted and eventually forgotten.

The conversation had run in the same heated, frustrating circles every evening but, as this was to be their final night of the first week, the pressure to fix Sasha's situation was reaching a rolling boil. In seven short days they would all be returning to their different cities, and it would be unlikely they would get to see one another again, as a group, until the new year. And who knew what Sasha would do in that time.

'It's like she's a different person.' Jade looked at the house as she said it. The white organza curtain drawn across the window on the upper left of the house – Sasha's room – filled momentarily and billowed outwards.

'She's better though. Than she was, I mean. There's still time for her to force us to learn a dance routine yet.' Erin looked at the group for agreement. They nodded with varying degrees of certainty.

Day bled into night, huge rivers of dusky pink seeping slowly upwards into a pale, then inky blue. Insects that sheltered in the bushes lining the property sang their delights at the disappearance of the sun, the quiet of the day descending into a chirping chaos.

Yasmine was standing at the head of the table, her features slightly tinged green by the citronella candles that burned all around them. The others slouched in assorted modes of indulgence, having just gorged themselves on two rotisserie chickens. She held a small, yet full, wine glass out and in front of her.

'What a week. What a year—'

'And we're only halfway through!' Claudia interrupted. Erin snaked one arm over Sasha's shoulders.

'Exactly. Halfway. Which, the way I see it, is just about the best way. It's not the end,
and it's not the beginning – we've still got time to do the things we want to, and the things we don't are halfway done! But all of it, any of it, none of it,' she laughed. 'I don't know – I'm *pissed*. What I mean is thank *God* we've got each other to do it with, eh?'

They brought their glasses together clumsily, each making sure to hold eye contact with another for a second before moving on, wine sloshing over the rims and onto the empty plates below.

Once they had cleared the table of the chicken carcasses, Sasha picked up the deck of well-thumbed playing cards Erin brought on every trip. The others watched her through woozy eyes as she shuffled the deck with all the ease and speed of a professional. This was the first time this trip she had engaged in their evening games.

'Blackjack?' she asked them. 'I'm dealer.'

'Definitely,' Erin responded, a little too enthusiastically.

Sasha dealt the cards, placing one face down and one face up in front of each of her friends.

She paused, then rested her hand on top of Erin's. She took a breath, certain that the rest of them could hear it rattle around her chest.

'I know I'm not doing what any of you think I should be doing–'

'That's not—' Jade tried to interject, but Sasha continued.

'—I'd be frustrated with any of you, too. And I'm sorry. For any anxiety or whatever that I've caused.' Her eyes were flitting around the group, not daring to settle on any of the four pairs that stared back at her. 'But I'm dealing with it. In my own way, y'know. And,' she glanced at Yasmine, trying not to smile, 'it's actually made me grateful for the first time ever that my mum is dead.'

Jade let out a low moan and dropped her head on to the table.

'I know that's bleak but it's true.'

'That better not be your silver fucking lining,' Yasmine said, her voice lower than a whisper.

Sasha grinned at her friends. It was the first time she had smiled, properly smiled, in a long while.

'No, it's not. The silver lining is that my arse looks fucking great in the video.'

The Looking Glass

Lindsay N. Evans

Dear Detective Inspector,

Please find enclosed what I think is a diary entry, which I found under a ruined floorboard after last week's break-in. It looks like there may have been an entire book under the floorboards, but this, a few ripped pages with nothing but scribbles, and a leather book cover are all that was left when I found it.

I'm not sure how much use this will be, but there must be some truth to the story as the recent renovations exposed the same silver mentioned at the end, which covers almost an entire wall of the sitting room, and a few (now broken) floorboards.

Please find the entry as follows—

I never intended on being buried alive before the age of thirty. Yet, late one Tuesday evening in the depths of November, I found myself digging away at the clay and loam above my head. It was damp, filling my nose, my mouth, my senses. My eyes shut tight against the weight of soil, which was lodged beneath my fingernails for days afterward, a nuisance of a reminder of what I had lost, and what I had gained.

At this juncture in my life, I thought I had understood both loss and gain. By the age of twenty I had gained myself a husband, and by twenty-one had lost interest in the man entirely. What I had believed to be a benign nature in my husband before the marriage, I soon discovered was simply indifference masquerading as concern towards the world. My feelings – or lack thereof – I discovered, were mutually shared. I, he told me, was not as pretty in the light of our sitting room as I had been in the ballroom in which we met. And, to his disappointment, I was rather difficult to order about, as I was rather content to say the word he had very seldom heard in his life: no.

The marriage, however, afforded me not only a title and the income to go along with it, but also provided access to the very thing I had sought since childhood: London society. My presence, in turn, diverted the critical gazes that looked down upon my husband's former rakish manner. The benefits of our union, we decided, outweighed its shortcomings. And a married man, we discovered, still had access to enough mistresses – or lovers – to keep himself entertained.

Together, we kept up the facade of a happy marriage while hardly interacting with each other, crossing paths only seldomly in the sitting room, where I often observed him gazing with contemplative regard into the mirror he had placed there not long after our nuptials. I had loathed it from the moment he brought it down from storage.

It was a hideous thing. Dim, tarnished silver snakes twined around its circumference, winding tighter and tighter as if constricting prey. Blackened flowers with drooping and torn petals scattered amongst the thorny vines that wove between them. It looked like something from a crypt, not belonging to the world of the living. Even the mirror's surface was mottled with age, blotches of corrosion spreading across the glass, rendering the piece almost unusable.

However, despite my protests against it, he insisted that it remain. And so the mirror clung to the wall in shadow, seemingly absorbing the surrounding light. No matter the temperature of the room, it was cold to the touch, so cold it once burned the tender skin of the maid I tasked with polishing it. Undeterred by my persistent objections to it, my husband adored the mirror, spending evening after evening looking into it as if it were a replacement for my lost affection.

It was in those moments that, after I had swung open the door on its silent hinges – my entering the room yet unbeknownst to him – I began to see the change in him. First came the wild energy that raged behind his eyes when he finally looked away from the mirror. Some nights, upon hearing my footsteps, he would look at me with no recognition in his gaze, only the glazed stare of a violent drunk. For weeks, I had thought he had begun drinking too much, but when I emptied the decanters, nothing changed.

One evening, I asked him how he could see anything through its degradation. He ignored me for a moment, then spoke.

'I see myself perfectly, my dear, if a little blurry. See,' he pointed at his reflection, 'there is the dimple on my left cheek. My hair is brown and my eyes are green. The mirror functions superbly.'

I let go of the fact that his dimple was on the right side of his face, not wanting to point out that he had again confused such a simple concept as right versus left. I thought nothing more of the interaction until that evening. My husband's eyes, I remembered suddenly, were blue rather than green. He never was the best with details, it was possible he simply misspoke. Though he also very rarely called me *my dear*, not since our courtship, but I let that fact slide as well. I was not one to fret over such small matters.

Then the muttering began. One evening, as I passed by the closed doors of the sitting room, my husband's voice filtered through the heavy wood. Our housekeeper passed by and I enquired with whom he spoke.

'I'm sorry, my lady, I am not aware of any visitors,' she told me.

'He must be rehearsing his next speech against the Trades Union, then,' I reassured her, though I did not myself believe it.

When she continued down the hall, I moved to my knees in front of the door and put my ear to the keyhole. The carved swirling patterns in the wood bit into my cheek, but I wedged myself closer, willing the sounds of the house to quiet.

'I cannot,' he was saying. 'I am not ready.'

Ready for what, I pondered.

'No! Not now!' His outburst filled the hall and I staggered away from it, landing soundly on my behind. I pushed to my feet as the doors swung open and collided with the walls.

I went to touch his arm. 'Are you alright?'

He slipped out of my grasp. 'I am quite fine.' He began to turn away, but faced me again, leaning in to kiss my cheek. 'Everything is fine, my dear.'

When I glanced into the sitting room, it was empty and everything was in its rightful place except for the mirror which rested crookedly on the wall. I took my handkerchief and tilted it back into place. The glass surface was fogged, inky smears reflecting into itself and my image came back to me in pieces, yet still tall, pale, and worn, entirely normal. I feared my husband had begun to lose his senses.

He continued to speak to himself in the sitting room over the following weeks. Early mornings or late nights, it mattered not, I often encountered him staring into that damned mirror and mumbling incomprehensible nonsense. The library swiftly became my favourite room in which to take my tea, as it was at the opposite end of the house and had walls thick enough to block out any sounds of his murmurings. But soon the staff became wary of him and my concern grew. I was no devotee to the institution of marriage, but the gossip he wrought on the house was intolerable.

He became agitated, short-tempered. But worse, his indiscretions quickly became public. On a walk through town, I watched him jostle others out of his way. I followed behind quickly, offering apologies.

To my horror, as I was mere steps away, I witnessed him snatch an unknown woman away from her husband, running his hands along the seams of her dress until she tore out of his grip. He even narrowly avoided knocking me into the path of a carriage, a stranger grabbing my arm at the last moment to prevent me from sprawling under the horses' hooves. It was only later that I began to believe he had acted intentionally.

It came to a head the morning before I awoke, buried in a fresh grave. I dressed to visit our solicitor, intent on voicing my concerns over my husband's recent behaviour. Though I could handle his temper, the public outbursts were creating more of a spectacle than I could keep up with. Being the centre of attention was not the issue, the societal gossip that said perhaps I made him act this way was.

But as I made my way through the halls of our sepulchral house, I neglected to be conscious of my surroundings. The plush carpets beneath my silk slippers muffled my steps, but they treated my husband in equal measure as he stalked behind me. As I neared the top of the stairs, rough hands met my shoulders. He pushed, and I fell. I grappled for the railing as I went down, twisting my body to face him. Green eyes seemed to glow from the low lustre of the burning lamps and a smile twisted his mouth into a severe shape, a dimple dotting his left cheek. The memory of that face bearing down on me was my last before waking crushed beneath the weight of the silty ground.

Fresh air greeted my fingers as they breached through the final layer of earth, the night cool and dry against my clammy skin. Slowly, so slowly, I clawed my way out, pulling my body along the ground until my feet came free. I lay there, catching my breath while watching the stars shift in and out of clouds. They winked, snuffing out one by one before returning once more.

My body ached, ribs protesting all movement as my head throbbed and the cloying sense of betrayal clung to the shallow grave from which I had just crawled. My husband, it seemed, had at last taken the final steps to rid himself of my presence. I had hoped that one day he would make a widow out of me, but I was disinclined to return the favour. Fortunately for myself, I was not so easily divested of life. The decision was made right then: he would pay for his insolence.

Moist soil soaked my clothing through, layers of cloth tinged brown, all the way down to my chemise. A shame, for I had put on my favourite walking dress that very morning. I sighed. No amount of washing would ever get it back to its original hue of deep rouge, it would have to be replaced, another thing for which I could blame my husband. The list grew longer with each passing day: poor character, terrible taste in décor, an attempted murder, and now a ruined dress.

I caught my breath and used a nearby gravestone to pull myself to my feet, taking in my surroundings. The graveyard was one near our home, he hadn't even bothered taking me further. Feeling along my right leg, I checked for the knife I had secured there earlier that morning. It was in its place, untouched. My husband was even more foolish than I had thought; what about my demeanour told him that I would go away without so much as a fight?

The house was dark as I approached, only the windows of the sitting room offering a dull glimmer at the edges of their curtains. I moved to his study window, easing it open and drawing out the knife. It filled me with a sense of righteousness, awakening my senses as the ruby at its base caught the light of a nearby oil lamp. I climbed through.

The sitting room awaited with its doors unlocked. A glimpse inside showed it in ruin, cushions strewn across the floor, torn to shreds. Feathers dusted the surfaces of the tables. The settee sat upended in a splintered mess, its front leg torn off. A maid with her duster still clutched in hand cowered in the corner, her sleeve ripped, the fabric quivering with her fluttering hands.

And standing at the dreaded mirror was my husband. He had a hand raised to its surface, touching it. No, I realised. He was not touching the mirror, but reaching *into* it. His hand sank to the wrist in its corroded surface, a sight so impossible I could not wrap my mind around it.

I must have made a sound, for he turned with a jolting movement to stare at me with those glowing green eyes.

'You,' he hissed. His voice was deeper, raspier than it had been just a day ago. When he raised a hand to point at me, I realised two things. The first: the hand raised was metallic, reflecting the glare of the burning lamps and throwing glinting shards of light across the room. Like the surface of the mirror, it too was blighted. The second: one of us was not going to make it out of this alive.

He lunged at me and I threw myself to the side, putting the card table between us as he tripped over discarded pillows.

'*My dear*, you do not seem yourself.' Part of me reveled in the thrill of the fight. This was the first moment of excitement I had experienced in our marriage.

Moving faster than I had ever thought possible, he leapt over the card table and rammed into my chest, pinning me back against the wall. His forearm came up to press into my neck as his rancid breath caught in my nostrils. From the corner of my vision, I saw the maid dash through the door.

'You were supposed to stay buried,' he whispered into my ear, breath clammy on my skin. 'But you never do as you're told, do you?'

He pressed harder and my world began to darken. Black spots flooded my vision but with a final burst of energy, I buried the knife in his stomach.

My husband stumbled back, the gilded ruby hilt protruding from his heaving torso. I leaned against the wall as I took shuddering breaths, rubbing the bruise his elbow had left on my clavicle. As I watched, waiting for him to collapse, he instead grasped the knife with both hands and yanked. It slid out of his body with a sickening gurgle and fell to the ground. Green eyes met my own and burned even brighter.

Perhaps, I began to think, I had underestimated him.

In a final moment of desperation, I seized the broken settee leg from the ground. He stepped back in anticipation of my swing, but I aimed not at him, but at his precious mirror. It connected solidly with the surface and spiderweb cracks spread outwards. My husband screamed and collapsed. I swung again and the mirror shattered, but rather than falling to the ground, the shards instead turned molten, dripping down the wall in silver streaks. It collected on the skirting board, coating the wood in a solid, metallic sheen.

I sank onto one of the ruined sofas. The room – a favourite of mine – was destroyed and my husband's body lay crumpled on the floor, a pool of molten silver spreading from him. The night afterward was marred by confusion as I attempted to piece together what had happened; no amount of rest could take my thoughts away from it, from the sudden freedom that had been thrust upon me.

I did not move as constables flooded the room. An intruder, I told them, and it was hardly a lie. An intruder had entered our home and caused this, thrown me outside, and murdered my husband.

I played the role of the newly-widowed to perfection. My former maid, who had immediately begun nonsensical ramblings to the police about demons and mirrors, conveniently wound up in Bedlam upon my good word to the principal physician.

When the whole mess was settled, I sat on a new settee in that same sitting room. 'He would have been happy to know,' I told those who came to offer condolences, 'that his widow is cared for so by your company.'

After the investigation and the funeral, and the cleaning of the mess, I was dismayed to see that the silver coated more of the sitting room than I had thought. It stained the wall in long stripes, like arms reaching towards the ceiling, sinking into the floorboards as well.

I have hung my grandmother's portrait in place of the mirror. It is not a favourite of mine – my mother's mother had been a dreadful woman with an awfully crooked nose and eyes set too far apart – but the colours had always matched the room well. When I hung it up, I had thought the silver to be trivial enough to ignore, but my newfound freedom must have distracted me, for as I look at the portrait now, I can see that the silver coats almost the entire wall, setting off my poor grandmother's eyes and making them an almost lively emerald rather than their true blue.

Sometimes, looking into those eyes, I am reminded of my dear husband. Sitting here, I think of him. My dear, my dear, my dear.

He never called me that after our marriage.

My dear.

I tried to photocopy the entry for you, but for some reason it wouldn't work. The ink may be too old for the machine because it couldn't pick up anything at all and just kept printing out solid grey sheets.

I want to thank you again for your help with the break-in. As you know, nothing valuable was taken, but the torn and stained wallpaper took almost a week to replace. Fortunately, it's finally done.

Please let me know if anything comes of this – I'll confess to being extremely intrigued by the story.

Sincerely,
M—

Cutting Down Trees

Paulina Schaeffer

Repentance. Some of the first memories of my life are shaped around the feeling of repentance, the feeling of having said or done something that gnaws at you from the inside, eating you up. So many times I could have spoken up. At the quiet kitchen table in the morning, hauling my parents out of their separate universes of thought, or at the dinner table in the evening, disrupting the careful phrases thrown back and forth. But the world isn't one side or another and, in the end, I never did. I was like a ghost floating around saying yes and amen to every question asked. It was tiring.

I looked out of the window and saw the world move by in slow motion. The train was taking on immense speed, carrying us through fields and forests and cities in what seemed like a second. Still, it felt strangely slow and peaceful to sit there and watch, not at all stressful or fleeting. Sometimes, feelings can be stronger than the physics of movement and the knowledge of facts. Fact was, however, that as soon as I got off the train, the world would stop moving altogether and at the same time take on enormous speed again. They were waiting for me. It had been a long time.

They would pick me up from the station and lead the way to their parked car, driving off with me into isolation. Their house was so far out that nothing disturbed the silence; it was like a hideout. Not even the few neighbours made a difference.

When I was younger, I loved going out there every summer to spend my holidays with them. For a time, I felt like every other child visiting their grandparents. It was different now. I didn't know why I had agreed to stay at their place or why I was going to their neighbour's funeral at all. Somewhere inside me, after seven years, a spot of weakness had begun to sprout.

I turned away from the window. My neck had gone sore already. The woman opposite me was knitting socks with turquoise-coloured wool. She was almost done with the first, a dwarfish L-shaped form swinging in the air, propelled by her fast light-hearted movements. Perhaps she would give them to one of her grandchildren. When she had entered the train alongside me and chosen the seat facing against the direction of travel in our four-seat compartment, she had seemed strangely familiar. I could almost grasp the image of her and match it to one of my memories. But she slipped away as soon as the memories were about to crystallise. She looked old and fragile in her grey, worn-out pullover but at the same time exuded a feeling of immense strength and security. It was as if we understood each other perfectly well just by looking in opposite directions. I knew that as soon as she got off the train, I would regret not having talked to her.

My grip tightened around the letter in my hand. The paper was no longer smooth like it must have been when Grandma had held it in her hands, filling blankness with words. It had gone crinkly with the edges creased and the back imprinted with my greasy fingerprints.

The train stopped and people were replaced by others. A man in a black suit and gelled hair took the seat next to me. He greeted me with a cold smile before focusing on his newspaper. He skipped the first pages featuring the local news and stopped in the business and economy section.

I imagined him with his black suit as one of the guests at the funeral, interrupting his busy life for a day or two, saying goodbye to a distant acquaintance, nothing too dramatic. He couldn't be more than an acquaintance; the deceased hadn't had close contact with anyone for a long time, except his two nurses. That much I knew, but nothing more. Probably, my seat neighbour was just visiting family or was on a business trip. The possibility of him being one of the guests was ridiculously small. There wouldn't be many people anyway. The small congregation in the hollow hall of the church, cut flowers carelessly draped over the backs of empty chairs that he would have preferred to see blooming in the soil. My grandparents blending in with the few other neighbours, all together on one side, and his carers reassuring the two or three cousins that stood as the rest of the family.

I pictured him dead. His hands, gnarled but strong, had always been covered in soil. His hair had looked messy, curls sticking out from everywhere, a labyrinth of roots. Standing tall, he had a deep, calm voice, like the wind's rustle through the branches of the woods. We hadn't been close but he had sometimes stopped by to talk to Grandfather about the crops that were almost ready to harvest. He had sometimes borrowed our spade, when he had broken his again while trying to dig out a particularly big root left from one of his trees. Birch trees. He had had to cut them down because they had fallen ill. When the trees were gone and it got dark outside, we could see the light of his living room window far out in the distance; our closest neighbour.

'Excuse me?' The man to my right was looking at me with raised eyebrows. 'Can you open the window, please?'

I considered refusing his wish. I didn't want to please him. My hand found its way on its own to the handle, avoiding an argument.

Would there have even been an argument? How could I have known? I didn't even try.

We were passing a row of neat and tidy gardens, accommodating little houses, sheds, ponds, and flowerbeds. The houses were so close that I could see the inhabitants sitting at their kitchen tables or on their couches watching TV. It felt wrong to see through their windows just as it had felt wrong when the trees were gone, and we could see inside our neighbour's home. It had felt like spying, although I never intended to. My eyes had sought the trees every time I'd looked, their broad and wide shadows replaced by clumsy chunks sticking out of the earth. I missed the change of colour from one day to another, their repetitive routine every year, warning me that it was soon time to go home, that another summer had ended. I knew he missed them too. He had told me so one day when he came to talk to Grandfather. Although I was young, I could feel his love for plants, the same love Grandma had in her.

It was during our evening strolls – when Grandfather would stagger a couple of steps behind us, only reluctantly leaving the car – that the shadows in Grandma's face would lift and her passion took control of her. She would grow and blossom like the flowers in her garden. Walks watered her, giving her all she needed to breathe, to come alive. She'd always joked around with me, taken me to the side of the path to show me the cicadas or the trace of a mouse in the grass. She pictured the future with me, a little garden for myself in which I would grow vegetables just like she did. *Always take orange trees inside for the winter. Never put leeks and beans together in one bed.* Darkness always fell before we could make it to the car, strolling off further and further. Grandfather's mumbled complaints behind us, his toxic breath, were swallowed by the forest around us or the wide fields ahead.

Another train passed ours, so close I thought we would collide. Rattling, shaking, bolting. I saw a flash of light and was transported back to the place where it had happened. I heard the creaking of car tires and smelled burnt rubber. Grandfather cursed, Grandma shrieked, the words *he's unconscious* circled in my mind. I had stayed in the car, a cold crawling down my body, making me stiff and unable to move. They had carried the man's heavy body like a lifeless tree trunk, plunging it onto the rear bench next to me, his messy hair brushing against my leg. He had been too big to lie on it completely; his legs were partly on the floor, not like the cats and dogs and bunnies Grandfather usually transported to and from his clinic in the car. One of his arms had fallen down from the seat, his knotty hand hung loosely in the air, dangling left and right as soon as Grandfather started the car again.

My train's compartment with the knitting woman blurred in front of me as raindrops smacked against the windowpane and my thoughts started spinning. Grandma crying, Grandfather shouting. No ambulance, there would be no ambulance. Back home, him lying on the couch. Motionless. Faint breathing. No doctor, just us. Grandma taking my hand, leading me away, far away from Grandfather's commands. Protecting me but what about him? I was the only one still hoping he might be okay. But of course, I needed more than hope to sneak into the living room again, pick up the landline, and ring the doctor or my parents. I needed strength that I didn't have at the age of twelve. How quickly hope could turn into despair and repentance. Miraculously fast.

The sound of the raindrops had evolved into a homogenous crackling, faster and faster until I could not distinguish single drops anymore. Next to me, the man in the black suit creased his newspaper laboriously until it was a crinkled piece of paper like the letter in my hand. He stuffed it in his briefcase and got up when the train came to a halt. And just like that he walked away. Away from the funeral he had never been invited to. At least I wasn't walking away anymore. I was facing it. The moment Grandma's letter had reached me, something inside me had loosened up. Had it been the certainty that she still loved me? She had taken a piece of the burden from my shoulders and put it onto hers. It had always been there, of course, but it wasn't until I read her letter that I realised. This was my chance to repent, to face the past and finally move on. Where to?

We were rattling on, advancing closer and closer. I shut the window. The woman opposite me had started reading a heavy-looking book. I looked down to the letter in my hand, where Grandma said she was sorry. I tried to imagine her sitting at her desk in the gloomy study writing to me. Her blue slippers, protecting her feet from the fresh breeze that the old windows could never shut out completely. The living room, the only warm place in the house, heated by the glowing timber in the fireplace. Was the shelf next to the fireplace and behind the dining table still filled with beer glasses? Was there still the sound of clinking glass bottles when opening the fridge in the kitchen?

Grandfather might have quit drink-driving, but I could tell from Grandma's letter that he had not abandoned the habit of drinking as such. The rushed handwriting told the story of their past, in places almost indecipherable as if written in haste, out of impulse, without his consent. She took the blame for what had happened. She should have spoken up, she should have called an ambulance against Grandfather's will. Even as a vet he could not have been sure that paralysis was the only option for the injured. But Grandfather had chosen for it to be. He had sold his clinic, the letter said. He was living with the consequences. Was he really? Easy for him to say. He who had gotten away with it, the hero, rescuing a neighbour from a driver who had hit and run.

Hit and run, hit and run, hit and run.

The train shot through a forest and the light turned warm and orange, sun rays peeking through the crowns of trees. Golden leaves were flying by the window, having left their loyal custodians to go on a journey by themselves. Spring and summer had raised them, autumn had dressed them, now winter was calling them.

Memories were passing by. Grandma stroking my hair, Grandfather repairing the swing, the dinner table set, a glass of lemonade on the veranda, the armchair, a warm summer's breeze, carrying the smell of disinfectant.

The next stop was announced. My stop. It came too abruptly and with such weight that breathing felt hard. The woman opposite made no move to pack her bag. I didn't want to leave the comforts of her presence. Her silent understanding. With every heartbeat, the train decelerated, bit by bit, step by step. A little boy ran past me, his parents following, laughing, ready to alight the train. I could see the station, the familiar clock hanging just beneath the spire of the tiny brick house where tickets were sold on weekdays. And behind, the empty square, only filled with life on a Sunday when the market booths were erected and craftsmen and farmers promoted their goods. The certainty of the train's halt arrived, that last pull of the brakes knocking me forward for a second. The doors opened and I could see the boy walk onto the platform clasping his mother's hand, the father struggling with their luggage for a moment before he caught up and reached for his son's other hand. By the brick house, two figures were standing together so closely they seemed to melt into one. Even from the train, I could make out Grandfather's hunched position and Grandma's supporting arm holding his. After all this time, she was still there to hold him.

You were only twelve years old, Grandma's words echoed through my head. And she was right. I had been a child, innocently stumbling into life just like the boy on the platform. Without guilt and repentance. Had I not stumbled enough? It wasn't my place to repent at the funeral, to be forced into guilt again. Grandfather had chosen their fate but he would not choose mine. Even though I longed for Grandma's hug, the sight of the two figures in the distance, entwined in alliance, kept me in my seat.

The acorn trees grouped around the marketplace had lost almost all their leaves, bare and bony arms reaching out into the sky. Yet they would be held again, year after year, by the leaves that spring and summer brought like little kisses over them. It was this inevitability that made the trees let go of their leaves without a single sense of fear. And it was this inevitability that reassured me; winter was calling me, taking me homewards. It was not my time to come and not mine to stay.

When the doors closed, the spot of weakness inside of me twitched before it slowly grew to heal. Before I knew it, I had asked the woman opposite about the book she was reading.

'It's Grimm's collection of fairy tales,' she said. 'You probably know them? Do you have a favourite?'

At home, a little orange sapling on the kitchen table was waiting for the summer to come, yearning to take its place on my balcony in the sun.

Waiting for Sunrise

Harry Clough

A meadow's silver haze, a breath to shake off
The chills of suspended night.
Lonely pigeons chuffing through the woods
Call miles and miles, each a connected wing.
Barbed dew on barbed wire on dew-laden
Fences slice through the woodpecker's strikes.
Dotted clouds hang illuminated, like poised
Blood shot with diamonds
On the cusp of turning amber.

The tallest tree, my reference for hasty confirmation.
Not yet a glow, the morning star still slumbers
Just out of sight.
Wet garden furniture wiped, breaking the millions
Of drops poised on their tender surfaces.
The world beyond doesn't exist or begin
In the still night where spider looms and
Catacombs, equal burial places, reflect
What lumbers on weary joints skywards.

A Muted Act

Harry Clough

We promised dawn's light breath would touch our faces
Before we went to bed. By sea, the dark
Night stretched for hours without a hint of gold
To light up grey horizons. Faces stark
Against a lighter's flame, we smoked and smoked
And talked and talked, lies tumbling from my ears.
The feeble flame listened, but as I choked,
It disappeared, leaving me with my fears
That pulsed against a trawler's light. Is this
Fair? I sit rejected but you keep me close
To hand, a useful thing, and it was bliss,
Until I knew that loving hurt the most.
We did not stay to see the dawning sun
But slunk back home to sleep as day began.

Haar

Kathia Huitron Moctezuma

The cold, wild wind sneaks through the sleeves of your coat and makes you tremble. It plays with your hair, tussles it. You fight it and it crashes into you with rage, pushing back your every step, as revenge. You beat it in the end, or maybe it grows tired of you and leaves. You walk by the rainbow-coloured doors of the houses on Shore Road. You see yourself reflected in the glass of the many windows you pass, and you imagine the city soundly sleeping, warm and quietly snoring, oblivious to the outside world.

The cobblestone streets echo your footsteps and the lamplights lead a straight path towards the water. Each breath you take sends clouds towards the sky. Your body is shaking, though not from the cold. You look for prying eyes that might be suspicious about the 3 a.m. walks, but you find none.

You reach the shore as the sky darkens, and you sit on an ocean-facing bench and wait. They will come. You see it at a distance, the devouring cloud that the wind is pushing towards you. Just a few more minutes. Your face is serene, yet your heart is racing, almost as if to meet the fog, impatient.

Half of the bridge is gone now, and the other side of the shore is sheltered from the only eyes watching, which are yours. They begin to take form as they step on the sand and surround you. You cannot see anything beyond the smoke-like cloud, except shapeless figures that begin to speak over each other, like a thousand songs playing out of sync. Sometimes you wish others could see them too; sometimes you envy those who don't.

His laughter rises over the voices and then you see him. He is running along the water, barefoot. He looks as he always looks, a lot like your nine-year-old brother, but also a bit like a memory of him, a bit lifeless. But then again, he's dead.

'Catch me, Adam, catch me,' he shouts. You're not as young as he remembers you. It's been more than a decade since he crossed the threshold into that unknown space he now inhabits. You know you can't keep up with his inexhaustible energy, nor with the overwhelming feelings that he leaves behind, as tornadoes leave paths of destruction. You go along because the last time you didn't, he was absent for weeks. The others start to scatter into town, through the streets and along the shore. More come, and some sit quietly, staring at the ocean, or what little of it they can see.

Kyle is running, but the strong winds keep pushing him back and swaying him in all sorts of directions, so he grows tired of trying and stops.

'I want to make a sandcastle now,' he says as he lets himself fall to the ground on his ass and then crosses his legs. He looks at you expectantly. You imitate him.

You try your best to make a solid, decent-looking castle, but your fingers are a bit numb from the cold of the water and sand. Kyle is looking at your hands with deep concentration; brow puckered, eyes squinting, analyzing your every move. He tries to pick up a handful of sand but his little fist comes up empty.

'It's not fair,' he complains, more sad than angry. You would pity him, except you know his little tantrums last but a few seconds. He goes back to staring at you. When you finish the last touches, he's already smiling with mischief.

'Now destroy it!' he cries like a man going into battle, raising his hand into the air, as though holding a sword.

'Your wish is my command, sir,' you reply, standing straight and saluting like a real soldier would. He giggles.

You kick the castle down, as Kyle laughs hysterically next to you. You laugh along with him, and it is as if you are eleven again, playing pirates with him, fighting and then making up without so much as a glance of complicity, pursuing new mischief together.

He stamps his feet on the rubble, though you're both perfectly aware it does nothing. This time, he does not mind that all his efforts are futile.

'Can... we... play hide-and-seek?' he asks, his hands behind his back, his grey eyes carefully assessing your countenance.

The sole mention of the game sends you into a shock-like state. All you can do is recall that dreadful afternoon you were playing on the cove.

Kyle had wanted to play one more time before going home, and you'd agreed because you didn't want to fight. You had leaned on the salt-covered stonewall, eyes closed, slowly counting to twenty. The tide had risen and the coming storm shook the sea into rage. You sneaked a cheating glance when you saw him running into the cave. Ever since, you've wondered whether you could've saved him if you had dived after him, even though it was almost immediately after getting caught by a wave that Kyle disappeared underwater.

'I need to rest now,' you say and sit on the wet stone of the steps leading to the beach. He sits beside you, shifting his attention from the others to the sea, from the sea to you. You check your watch, it's almost seven. Kyle is dangling his feet over the edge of his seat, rocking back and forth with impatience. He wants to keep playing, you know, but your body is tired and aching, and your spirits have plummeted. Perhaps he knows, he's always been mature for his age;

perhaps he's taking care of you too by just sitting, almost touching, exuding warmth though he is made of cold winds.

'It's almost dawn,' you say with a hint of panic mingled with sadness. Your brother nods. The break of day is always the hardest, especially not knowing when you'll see him again. But every night you come to the water and wait. The nights he does not show feel like losing him all over again to the ocean: the terror of knowing him gone and unreachable, the sudden flow of tears and then the numbness that follows hopelessness. That is the worst, the most dangerous, the one that makes you wonder if you're the ghost.

'What happens when you leave here? Where do you go?' you asked him once, when the overwhelming sensation of loss overpowered you. He crossed his arms, tipped his head to the side and pondered for a few seconds.

'I don't think I can explain it to you.'

'Try,' you pleaded, teary-eyed.

He shook his head. 'You'll see. Someday.'

The others start to come back to the shore as the sky is beginning to shift colours, a slight pink is starting to appear and you can see them more clearly now, though they look slightly more faded. You take a last look at him, at all of them, almost wishing to join them, but you know Kyle would never forgive you if you tried a second time. You pass your fingers over the rope burns of your neck, remembering. If only you had succeeded that day...

The wind caresses the sea and then your skin, gently, as if comforting you. You don't cry, not because you don't want to, but because Kyle is looking at you with a tender, serene smile that makes him look wise, wiser than you perhaps. You would hug him if you didn't know all too well the hurt of it being in vain.

The sun begins to rise and the others slowly dissipate. Your little brother begins to vanish and you exhale the night away, holding on to the hope that maybe tomorrow you'll see him again.

Lady Curenandefal
an excerpt

Simon West

No one is quite sure of the origin of the Curenandefal family name. There is some talk of it being a corruption of Coromandel, a peninsula of New Zealand, itself named after a British Royal Navy vessel which stopped there in 1820 to purchase kauri spars. However, the derivation of Curenandefal from Coromandel would be so wild a corruption in so short a period as to cause serious-minded people alarm, and so, as a theory, it is widely rejected. The ship itself derived its name from the Coromandel Coast of India, so called by seventeenth-century Dutch sailors who stopped at that place for water, and who, with the characteristic carelessness of the coloniser, mispronounced the indigenous name, which was Karimanal. The word Karimanal was possibly derived from Karai Mandalam, meaning The Realm of the Shores, but here we stray too far.

Some contest that the secrets of the origin of the Curenandefal name lie in dissection, and note the closeness of the second half, 'andefal', to the Portuguese 'adelfa', the feminine singular of 'adelfo', translated in English as 'oleander', the notoriously poisonous shrub. Lady Curenandefal is certainly a singular female and though perhaps secretly liking the idea of being notoriously poisonous, she has let it be known, in private circles, that she eschews the connection on account of the common English name for oleander being 'dogbane'.

The Latin 'Curia unde Fal' sounds similar and, though grammatically incorrect, may hint at a Roman citizenry hailing from a village in South Khorasan, an area which forms part of modern-day Iran. Again, Lady Curenandefal cannot be swayed on this one. It is not that she disapproves of classical derivations – far from it – but she has always been a little wary of being too closely associated with geographies that fall outside London's Belgravia; the Iranian Embassy is in Knightsbridge.

As a commentator, or compiler, or narrator of the circumstances surrounding the Curenandefal family, I feel I must, early on, declare an interest. Though I have been trained in impartiality, through the various courses and degrees outlined in the foreword to this work, I feel it is judicious to inform the readership that my own family's history has at times been inexorably linked to the Curenandefals, and not always for the good. In short, they ruined us. How this was achieved will, of necessity, form a not-insignificant part of the narrative of this volume. As a precautionary measure, and so as to attain the highest standards of impartiality, my text has been carefully reviewed by the editors so as to deliver into your hands a trustworthy and definitive work.

Philip closed the book and turned to his wife who lay on the sun lounger beside his. 'How's your book?' he asked.

'Fine,' she said without looking up. 'Yours?'

'Fine,' he said. 'A bit wordy though. Shall I order some drinks?'

'That'd be nice,' she said. 'Maybe a mango smoothie?'

'Yep. I'll press this button thingy.'

'Doesn't work,' said his wife without looking up. 'You'll have to go to the booth.'

'I'll try it anyway,' said Philip and he pressed the button on the WiFi remote on the table that was supposed to summon someone from the hotel to take orders.

'Look at that crack on the wall over there,' said Philip. He was squinting at one of the hotel's white walls on the other side of the swimming pool. 'Is that a crack?' he asked. His wife glanced up over her book.

'What are you talking about?' she asked.

'There,' he said, pointing, 'between that balcony with the lady and the skinny palm tree.'

'Don't know,' said his wife, returning to her book.

'Might be an expansion joint,' he said. 'It's very straight.' He continued to look at it. 'Hey! Maybe it's not a crack. Maybe it's a long, thin line of dried blood!'

'Really?' said his wife.

'Yeah. Maybe up there on the roof, on the flat roof where nobody ever goes, they do voodoo type stuff and that's where the blood drains off. Maybe it was a condition for building the hotel – that voodoo stuff could happen on the roof.'

'I don't think so,' said his wife.

Philip continued to contemplate the long dark line that ran all the way from the top of the building down four stories to an area of planting at the base of the wall.

'Oh I know!' he continued. 'Say it's not voodoo. Say it's the mafia. Say there's this guy and they bump him off and they want to get rid of the body and this hotel is being built, so the boss knows the foreman and one night they dump the body in the foundation and pour the cement on top and then the rest of the hotel gets built. But that means there's a weakness in the foundation, you see, where the body is, and one day the man's skull cracks, under the pressure, and that crack spreads all the way up the wall and there it is.'

'That's a bit grim,' said his wife. 'Is that drink coming?'

'I don't think the button works. I'll go.' He stood up, put his feet in his flip flops and, having taken a moment to feel less woozy in the heat, set off in the direction of the bar.

Philip and his wife Marjory, both in their early thirties, are holidaying in Fuerteventura, at a four-star hotel in the north of the island. This is their second visit to the same location. Their lives being ordinarily busy, they enjoy the chance to relax. Consequently, they take no advantage of the excellent opportunities for water sport afforded by the island's climate, nor do they take much interest in the unique volcanic landscape. As to Philip's speculations about the crack in the wall, these are, of course, nonsense. The crack is indeed an expansion joint; something he will see when he takes a stroll past the bar to inspect it. There is no formal history of voodoo in the Canary Islands, despite a strong Catholic tradition and proximity to the west coast of Africa, and although ritual human sacrifice continues to be recorded south of the Sahara, the practice has yet to spread to Fuerteventura. The idea of the mafia is less fanciful. It is known, for example, that the Rome-based 'Banda della Magliana' operate money laundering schemes in the Canaries. Again, however, Fuerteventura seems to be free of such activity and, in any case, as was said before, the crack is an expansion joint.

'That crack is an expansion joint,' said Philip, returning with a tray of drinks and nibbles.

'Splendid,' said Marjory, closing her book and sitting up to take her smoothie.

The unquestioning acceptance of the Curenandefal's position near the top of our Edwardian Society relies in small part on the short-term memory of crowds and in large part on the current Lady Curenandefal herself, whose careful machinations over a lifetime have all but obscured the labyrinthine tracks of her family's rise to prominence. So obscured are they, in fact, that it has not been without considerable effort that a rough history has indeed been compiled. Incomplete though this history may be, it serves to conclude that the Curenandefals have only enjoyed their current prominence for no more than the last four generations. Further back in time, behind these four vaunted generations, lie murkier histories with more convoluted paths. Wending one's way upon these paths one meets quite an oddment of characters. There is, for example, the sixteenth-century master of Trinity College, Oxford, a Reverend Dr Kettle, noted for his determined efforts, over many years, to extract sunlight from cucumbers.

Also of note, a certain Francesca Egerton whose vehemence in preferring the company of chickens over people was manifested each evening at table, where she dined with six of her favourite hens. And what should we say of George Wellsit, the inventor of a miniature pistol for shooting wasps? Not much, other than it is no wonder the current Lady Curenandefal has made it her business to cover the tracks, to paper over the cracks, to keep the skeletons firmly in their closets. Given that here some may have been exhumed for public view, it is my sincere hope that she is not too displeased; for who am I to lay the sins of the fathers at the feet of their children?

'When was this published?' said Philip to himself, flicking to the front of the book. There he saw that the first edition had been printed in 1904, that it had been included in Everyman's Library in 1967, and that the volume he held had been printed in 1998. He looked at the front cover. A portrait of Lady Curenandefal stared back at him imperiously; pince-nez gripping her bridge, jewels about her neck, her hair caught high in elaborate coiffure.

Philip glanced at his wife's empty sun lounger on his right; empty of Marjory, but still occupied by her abandoned paperback, its pink cover curling in the sun. This was the third day of their holiday and already she had become restless for other company. He looked over to the left and there she sat at the side of the pool. She was talking to someone. Apparently sensing she was being watched, Marjory turned to look at him and Philip had no time to pretend that he was absorbed in his reading before she beckoned. He sighed, put down his book and walked over to her.

'This is my husband Philip,' said Marjory to the lady who sat beside her at the pool's edge.

'Hello,' said the other lady in a strong Cockney accent. 'I'm Stacey. What's that book you've been reading, Philip?'

'Oh, it's not much really,' said Philip. 'I picked it up from the book-swap shelf, over beside the bar.'

'You're lucky,' said Stacey. 'I looked there yesterday, but they were all in German! Is that one any good?'

'It's a bit wordy but I'm enjoying it,' said Philip. 'It's the history of a London family.'

'Oh, I love history and London's proper riddled with it. It's amazing, honestly, I swear, every street has had something going on,' she effused. 'What family is it about?'

'They're called the Curenandefals,' said Philip.

'Oi, Geoff!' shouted Stacey, 'Do we know any Currentandyfulls in London? That's my husband Geoff,' she said, gesturing to a man in shorts sitting on a lounger. He had the tattoo of a bulldog on his chest.

'What you on about now?' he barked back.

'Don't be rude! Come over here and say hi to Philip and Marjory,' said Stacey.

Geoff stood up and was making his way over when a young boy hurtled past, slapped him on the leg, and then bombed into the pool.

'Oi, no running!' shouted Geoff at the boy, who was still below the water's surface. Now Geoff was closer, Philip could see that the tattoo was not of a bulldog, but was an attempted portrait of the boy.

'Hi, I'm Geoff,' said Geoff, extending a hand. 'What you on about babe?'

'Tell us the name of that family again, Philip,' said Stacey.

'It's the Curenandefals,' said Philip. 'They lived in Belgravia.'

'Never heard of them,' said Geoff.

'No, it's not that interesting really,' said Philip and he turned to watch the boy in the water. What the boy was doing couldn't be called swimming. Devoid of technique, he was attempting mastery over the element by the application of sheer force alone. The measure of his success was that he managed to keep his nose above the surface of the water more often than not.

'Look at him,' said Geoff, pointing. 'Proper makes me laugh!'

'Am I doing it, Dad?' the boy managed to shout mid thrashing.

'Nah! It's rubbish!' laughed Geoff.

'You're doing it wonderful, babe,' said Stacey to her son. 'Don't listen to him!'

'He'll get it eventually,' said Geoff to Philip, ''cos he can't drown, him.'

'He can't drown?' said Philip.

'No, he can't drown because of how he was born.'

'Because of how he was born?' parroted Philip.

'Yeah. When he was born, right, you wouldn't believe it, he was still in his sack!'

'In his sack?' said Philip with genuine shock.

'Yeah! It was like something out of *Alien*!' laughed Geoff. 'You ought to have seen it!'

'Sright,' said Stacey, responding to Marjory's shocked expression. 'So there I am, on the slab, a-heaving and a-puffing and blimey, I thought like I was gonna split in half! So I'm busying away and I glances up and, on my life, suddenly he's looking like he's watching some sort of horror film! Before he was all like, "Come on dahlin'! You're doing amazin'!" and all that, but he's standing there white as a sheet, when all of a sudden I've gone and given birth. But them midwives, suddenly they're all busy and looking proper shocked, and saying, "Well, well! This is a first!" Honestly, Marjory, I was that knackered, and the room was spinning as it was, what with the gas-and-air, but I summons it up and says, "What is it? What's the matter?" and him, he says, "Babe! The baby's still in its bag! You've squeezed the whole thing out in a one-er!"'

The birth phenomenon that Stacey is describing, when a baby is born inside an intact amniotic sac, is referred to in medicine as an 'en caul birth'. Caul refers to the part of the sac covering the baby's head. Due, perhaps, to the rarity of such births (fewer than one in eighty-thousand) its occurrence has attracted a certain amount of superstition; the most common and persistent belief being that those born 'en caul' are immune from drowning. As a result of this belief, cauls were once highly prized by sailors and were traded for large sums of money, right up until the eighteenth century. There is no evidence at all, however, that those who are born 'en caul' are protected in any way whatsoever from death by drowning.

Philip and Marjory were back on their loungers again. It was late afternoon and they were well-positioned for sunshine, the other side of the hotel being in shadow. The poolside was quieter now and the attendants were busy straightening sun loungers, removing towels, and cleaning the pool with long pipes and poles; erasing all signs of the activity of the day.

'They sell fruit,' said Marjory.

'Stacey and Geoff?' said Philip, genuinely surprised.

'Yes. They have a fruit stall at the new Covent Garden,' said Marjory.

'I would never have guessed they sold fruit,' said Philip. 'I've been to Covent Garden. Where's the new Covent Garden?'

'I don't know,' said Marjory. 'We should go to London sometime. I haven't been since I was a child.'

'I've never heard of that birth thing before, have you?' asked Philip.

Marjory laughed. 'No! Sounds horrendous!'

'And that kid can't swim,' said Philip. 'I don't think I'd trust an old wives' tale to keep my child from drowning.'

'He'll be fine,' said Marjory. 'Some kids are just robust. You can tell just by looking at them.'

'Do you think our kids would be robust?' asked Philip.

'Ours?' Marjory laughed. 'I doubt it! You and me?'

Philip turned from looking at his wife and found himself staring at the afternoon light reflecting off the surface of the empty pool. He sighed, picked up his book, and attended again to the history of the Curenandefals.

Naarm[1]

Sandeep Sandhu

His story began in the Season of Eels[2]. The spirit child[3] sprung into being as his mother toiled in the dusty heat, the body inside her grown enough to receive a soul but still too formless for the world outside her womb, like the water of life waiting to be liberated from the mountains. She knew it was a boy because the seed inside her had sprouted roots that connected her to the mycorrhizal network of creation, giving her the tools to see beyond what most could, even if just for a short period of time. It was as if she could count every grain in a handful of sand, a tactile belief that seemed inexplicable to anyone but her.

As the child gestated in her, she had no doubt he would grow up to do something momentous. Weeks passed – the Eels withered, the scorched earth greedily sucked down the ever more frequent rains,

---

[1] The traditional Boon Wurrung word for Port Philip and the surrounding area.

[2] Late summer – January to March.

[3] Pregnancy in many aboriginal cultures is not attributed to human contribution, but the unborn child is seen as the embodiment of some totemic-territorial aspect of 'Dreaming' – the order constituted by the ancestral creators.

and the stars began to shiver, dissolving in the sparse night sky; all the while, the child came closer to reaching the physical plane.

Labour began as the sunset gently draped sheets of orange and red across the land, making the Birrarung[4] shimmer, and she remained in a hospital as night fell and the river turned to wine, glistening with silver streaks under the moonlight. The boy was born with the sun, its awesome blaze reminding the world of its power despite its lethargic climb to the apex of the sky.

He was called Robert Kirk, his only signifier in the eyes of the state, although to his people he had many other names, some of which were known only to those in his clan. He grew up hiding in marshes and splashing in lakes, embedding himself into the muddy turf, plugging himself into the heartbeat of the hundreds of life forms that lived with him, entwined like stems in a wreath. Here, time would slow to a crawl, then a halt, dropping suddenly like the wind in the eye of a storm until he was ready to join the rhythms of human life again, a beat as energetic as it was brief.

His mother would encourage this exploration and exaltation of their landscape, warm pride flooding through her as she watched her son move deftly through nature like she imagined his ancestors had, though, the space they inhabited was ever-shrinking thanks to the unyielding encroachment of settlements that dominated the earth instead of working with it.

As the growth of his mind began to rival that of his body, he learned how to find the best segment of shore to spot burrunan[5], how to make the calls of the birds who he shared his territory with, and how to sing the songs that would guide him across the vast tracts of land that his people were once married to. Robert lived an idyllic life,

---

[4] The name of the Yarra River in Woiwurrung, the language of the Wurundjeri People.
[5] A species of bottlenose dolphin only found in VIC, Australia.

sheltered from what had been done to his ancestral land in the name of progress, but as he moved out into the rest of the world the weight of history began its inevitable sag onto him.

When he started school, his mother insisted on driving him herself as the bus route went the wrong way down a Songline[6]. To the settlers, roads were tools, neutral things. However, Robert and his mother saw these practical grey snakes as paving over the bones of a culture, replacing exquisitely crafted epic journeys that followed the stars in the sky with signs that dealt with the immediately tangible, severing human connection with the boundless.

Three years after he began formal education their remote region became beholden to the whims of greedy general store owners, who seized the opportunity to exploit a captive market who'd had their ability to live off the land ripped away. Soon, the hours his mother worked weren't enough to make ends meet if they wanted to carry as on as usual. Suddenly, perhaps, the Songlines had no place in the new world – it was enough to know how to navigate using modern tools instead of the stars and the landscape and the music of the past. Despite these rationalisations, the first time Robert stepped onto the bus, mother and child could hear the dismay as eons of ancestral knowledge were ignored. They gritted their teeth and ignored the slimy, cold sensations in their stomachs.

At school he didn't have the vocabulary to explain why certain things made his stomach boil and words get trapped in his throat.

_____

[6] Paths the great creators took when forming the land in Australia – can be across land and sky. Journeys are communicated via song, taking in landmarks and star formations.

Teachers would ignore his outstretched hand, exuberance pigeonholed as overconfidence or even aggression, instead of a passion for learning. It was almost never the children that gave him those particular looks moulded by years of spite and mistruths; not at first, anyway, until that same manufactured sense of superiority forced its way into their souls too.

After situations where the unfair realities of bigotry would leave Robert drenched in sadness, his mother would try to explain that the hostility came from a lack of education and a collective need to justify the horror of the past. However, without getting into the grittier, far-too-adult details of the recent history of his people, it was impossible to give him all the information he needed, and as such he would simply sweep away whatever indignity had happened that day, pushed aside until it got too big to be ignored again.

His evenings, however, were always joyous affairs. The blanket of belonging wrapped him tightly when he was back among the shining lakes and the vibrantly plumed birds and the boundless night sky. He would go to Corroborees[7] and talk to elders and friends, learning to socialise with his people. Soon he was able to do the same at school, as his peers reached an age where the prejudices of their parents were either hardened or abandoned.

Through what he perceived to be luck or circumstance – although it was mostly thanks to his mother and her otherworldly intuition – he avoided the pitfalls that many of the original inhabitants of the land fell into through bad luck and ill-circumstance: developing a dependency on intoxicants, gambling away what meagre items they had, and the resulting life of petty crime. She had always taken the time to introduce Robert to the worst of the alcoholics who stumbled around their town, so they were tangible to him instead of

---

[7] An Australian Aboriginal dance ceremony which may take the form of a sacred ritual or an informal gathering

a joke like they were to many other kids. He learned their condition wasn't an abstract, a morbid curiosity, but something that could wrap its tendrils around him until he was fully ensnared. She would also encourage him to work through the indignities of bad grades and unfair targeting by teachers who didn't believe people like them were capable of rising above savagery, let alone to the heady heights of academic achievement. This sense of injustice motivated him further, and his grades soon mirrored his work ethic.

He went to university to study law because he saw his people needed help navigating the new world they'd been forced into mere centuries ago; a drop in the river of time when your collective knowledge stretches back tens of thousands of years, yet a drop that had rippled along the length of the snaking river back to the source. Along the way, his eyes were opened by books he'd never imagined reading and whirls of intricate smoke patterns weaving their way towards the ceiling and the sweet, lightly perfumed skin of lovers. Although he and his mother now argued more about the state of their world and how to fix it, she was still proud, and still able to nurture the curiosity in him, even as his knowledge surpassed hers.

She would sit and listen to him wax lyrical for hours on all sorts of topics, allowing him to hone his ideas and oratory skills by peppering him with the questions of the curious and uneducated. He would watch on as her brow furrowed in attempted understanding, trying to anticipate her questions and then, eventually, learning it was best to let her finish asking something before trying to jump in. He learned that knowledge wasn't just in books or smoke patterns or the leather-scented offices of large-gutted pale men who turned red in the summer.

Robert accumulated accolades in his twenties and thirties, giving his life the appearance of a purposeful one. However, he would wake almost every night tangled in drenched sheets, terrified by dreams of a black tsunami rushing towards him, his feet rooted to a grotesque, orange version of the arid landscape he'd grown up with. In some versions of the nightmare he was allowed to turn, straining to rotate his body with every sinew he could, at which point he'd see an ever-growing ball coloured red and yellow, the monstrous sun closing in on him from the other direction. As he reached middle age, he realised he needed to do something more to alleviate this weight he felt, like mercury-tinged air that had seeped into him and rooted itself in his bones after that first bus ride all those years ago.

His nightmares jumped into reality, the sun moving to the heart of his fear. For so many it was considered the giver of life, whereas in the dry landscape his people called home, it wasn't as revered as running water or the ancestral creatures who had moulded the land, hacking and tunneling with stone-axes to reach the moorool[8] and free it from its mountainous cage. In some ways, it was even feared, its whipping harshness both destructive and everlasting.

His mother felt it long before Robert explained it to her, her well-tuned rhythms suddenly out of sync as basic tasks became more arduous. At first she thought it was her age – her body was not what it once was, now soft and pliable like an overripe fruit – but when plants started to wither weeks earlier than they normally did, she realised it was something beyond the stream of time ebbing away at her physical body.

It had always been hot, and it had always been dangerous. Now though, it was becoming more obvious. Even the settlers began to take notice, utilising their tools to measure just how much stronger the deadly glow was and figuring out why. Robert saw there was nothing holistic about their methods; even with his education and absorption of their ways and eventual, inevitable assimilation, he couldn't understand why they couldn't see what was, to him, a Rube-Goldberg machine of decimation. Nonetheless, they managed to

---

8 Big water - the source of the Yarra River that was once locked in the mountains

tighten the hole above his land that had allowed the most vicious rays of the sun to strike through. It was lauded as a success, any lessons on avoidance drowned out by the giddy joy of an apparent victory over nature.

The blinkered approach of the settlers was useful in some cases, but it was obvious the earth was still crying out for help. Their navel-gazing trained them to focus on the pieces instead of the whole puzzle, and now they were pointing excitedly at two of them connecting in the centre when there were still hundreds more to fit into place.

The settlers soon began to believe they could reverse the issues they'd birthed with their zeal without trying to understand the underlying cause of the issues, or making sacrifices to live more in tune with the Earth instead of battling against it. Robert could sense it would take years, possibly lifetimes, to undo the heinous actions they'd committed over the last century, although yet again he didn't have the vocabulary to express himself in what they would consider a coherent manner. So, he went back to university, this time so he could put nature's predicament into words that couldn't be lost in translation or batted away as the superstitious musings of a dying culture.

All this strife gave him more of an appreciation for what remained. It was true the lakes and marshes he'd grown up in had changed more in his lifetime than they had in previous generations, but they were still there, as was most of the flora and fauna he knew as intimately from his youth as he did the features of his own face.

His mother, too, remained, shrunken and weakened like their ancestral land, but still fighting on. On the ever-rarer occasions he would return, her cheeks would lift and she would flash her remaining teeth at the rumble of his car pulling in. Robert would spend his entire visit with her or in the marshes. The rest of the small settlement was in even more disrepair than it had been when he was a child – unfortunate addicts lined the streets so thickly it was impossible to visit one of the remaining non-pawn-store shops without stepping over another living being.

The human cost of progress might have been a lost cause for his generation, but Robert's optimism drove him to thoughts of salvaging what was left of the marshes and beyond. The mighty river still flowed like time. The markings that defined the Songline tracks were still there, and as long as that bond with the earth remained, hope would too.

But then came the bushfires. The flames were not birthed from cold fire[9], the technique his people had passed on for centuries, nor were they the result of the usual natural burning that restored energy to the earth – fire the land not only allowed for but craved. These were uncontrolled, angry flames that lashed out at the very life that sustained them. The damage was such that even the settlers were shocked into action. Many of them began to comprehend the problem wasn't to be tackled in one way or with one solution, although these people weren't the ones with the power to do anything about it. Nonetheless, the awareness of the bonds that shackled humanity and the earth together became more mainstream, even as the former ravaged the latter.

Robert took his mother out of the bush and kept her in the city for almost a month, where she would watch the sky yellow in the day like a dying magnolia, and then turn blood red at night under the insulating blanket of smoke. Robert, however, was more focused on the television than what nature was showing him, where there was talk of nothing but the fires from the media. A ripple of hope radiated through him as he started to believe those with the means to do something might listen to their sons, their daughters, and their peers. There was renewed vigour in his attempts to marshal further

---

[9] Low, closely monitored fires that only burn the underbush.

help, even as he became dependent on a walker and his hair frosted to the colour of the moon he'd once laid under night after night as it dressed and undressed in wisps of cloud.

He carried on with his fight when time devastated the balance of his life, as his mother lay dying back in his ancestral home. She clutched onto the last vestiges of a life that had been seeping out, and her final thoughts were of the work her son was doing, a swell of pride preceding the complete fall of her body. He was unable to attend any elements of the sorry business[10] in her honour, despite it lasting over a week.

He signed letter after letter and went to protest after protest, pushing through the spikes of pain that ripped through his limbs and the waves of regret that came alongside ignoring his ancestral duties in the name of a larger fight. When he was particularly low, he would flick back through his phone at the last pictures he had of him and his beaming mother, her chessboard smile carefree and full of pride, her eyes never looking at the camera but always angled towards her son, and that would reignite his hope. At points he even believed the government would pay attention to the warning signs he'd been pointing out for decades; he assumed with his legal and scientific training they would have to take him seriously, even if the bigotry that had been laid alongside their foundations was still leaning on all the decisions they made. He was sure the need to cover up their past that his mother had told him about would be superseded by the present and real threat of the flames licking at their door.

He knew it was too late when he went back to the lakes. He hadn't visited in years, and as he once again sat in the silence of the surroundings of his youth, there were no birds chirping and no Christmas Beetles scurrying about. The water was a murky brown, the dust and ash commingling in the sky and raining down mud. The

---

[10] English term for funeral rites across Aboriginal Australian cultures.

marshes exuded an odour that betrayed a profound lack of health. The flies were the only ones still thriving, surrounding the carcass of the area in which he'd learnt most of what he knew, feeding off the last vestiges of earthly energy that were still battling their way into existence. He dug his hand into the mud and felt no pulse of life, just an echo as the sound of his grasping hands bounced around the hollowness that inhabited what had once been full of promise.

He stayed there until night seeped into day, when in the clear dark skies he could just about make out Bunjil's campfire[11] flickering in the distance. He was cold, even in the still summer evening air, little shivers running through him like he was being chipped away by tiny stone axes. The chill settled inside him, shivers morphing into deep seizures that clutched his body like a sonic boom. Instead of shaking them free he let them bound freely through his already frail frame. Time no longer stopped for him here, no longer morphed into a sticky honey that oozed by or even stayed fixed, instead sweeping him along carelessly as it did for everyone else.

It ended on a hospital bed in what was once his ancestral land but was now a monument to modernity. The smoke from the fires had moved past the city the week prior and had already been forgotten by most. The doctors were unsure what had caused his heart to malfunction as dramatically as it had. Robert died at dusk, having done so much, yet having achieved so little – his final thought as he followed the arc of the sun and the heartbeat of the marshes.

---

[11] Jupiter.

Stone Silence

Harry Clough

I woke, rested and cool
and by a lake with
instructors holding oars
and wistful mangoes
smiling and demonstrating
how to row
to the hill
where we'd sit
and judge cattle.

Somewhere in the
back, all alone
with stone silence
you stood there,
lobster in hand
(lobster for hand?).
I can't remember
dodging like Perseus.
Please wake up.
Want to forget.
You followed me
you never spoke

you watched me
I loved you
you watched me
your stone silence.

I woke, unrested, hot and fighting
The muggy August scorch, flooded with
Draining images, each one lurched away
In turn, some gently, some frighteningly;
Water, hats, kayaks, lobsters (with hats?)

Leo

an excerpt from *Polly*

Ilaria Remotti

Pale blue. Charcoal. A pearly shine to the mist. Shell-pink stripes beginning to line the sky. Somehow the colours had escaped him through the years, slowly slipped away. They had grown blurry in his memory, buried under shrapnel and debris. Fog was rising from the moist soil of the garden, glowing in the watered-ink air of almost-morning.

The palace looked quiet. The terrace deserted but for himself and his footprints. If only it was snowing, he could at least be sure his tracks would disappear. Now they could still follow him. They could still take him back. He scanned the bushes, the trees, the slanted lane on the side of the house that led back down to the valley. He saw no life, no eyes. He listened closely to the garden's voices, the woodland's rasps. But there was no breath to hear. Sleet began to fall, dispersing the mist and tinkling like rice grains on the house's walls. He hoped for plumper flakes. He imagined how they would fill in the hollows of his boot prints in the ground, kindly hiding his way home.

He traced circles on the frosty terrace, hesitantly closing in on the walls of the palace, then stepping away. The house stared down at him through the tall glass door, but he dared not look through and into the room beyond. He strangled his hat with his fingers, twisting the fabric until the stitches loosened and threads poked from the seams. His eyes hurried from one panel to the other, fixating on the pink, charcoal, and pale blue, reflections of the garden and the sky behind. He stood wondering how he could just walk in, hoping she might have left, flown away with changing seasons. Perhaps it would be easier. After all, why would she stay?

He could see his own reflection silhouetted in the glass, dark against the mirrored garden like a black ghost, memories pouring out like blood from its wounded chest. Fresh oranges. Seashells. Foxes. Pollen. Grass strands woven to make pages for a book without a cover. Stories on the green pages, an ink that smelled like grape skins. Her freckles. Her cries as he marched away. The white gleam of their home in the distance as he left it behind.

Snow whirled harsh and icy around his head like a buzzing crown. The garden was so silent still, the road clear. Only the snow rang shrill against the palace walls, and the dread sat in the back of his mouth for a moment. They might not find him.

When he finally looked through, past the glass, into the room, it was almost by mistake. The furniture inside was hidden under white veils. The floor carpeted in dead leaves that must have made their way in through broken windows.

So she had gone. She had let the house die. She had let the garden dry out. If they had still been children, this could have been a game of hide and seek. Hiding was always thrilling, finding was always sweet.

He looked at the long table in the far side of the room, the familiar folds and cracks hidden under the cloth that covered it top to bottom, though it looked oddly distorted through the rapidly freezing glass. He thought of that one day, the day they had found rotten wooden crates in the cellar. He had sneezed and sneezed and sneezed. But she had bravely stuck her hand under the cover of one and yanked it open, revealing piles and piles of glass jars. Some still smelled of sugar so they had gone to wash them in the river. Then they had lined them up on the long table and filled them with twigs of herbs from the garden. Mostly rosemary and laurel leaves and thyme. She had always smelled of rosemary since then.

The table itself was a swishing ghost now, silenced and empty. A thin strand of gold peeked out from under the white linen on the floor.

Hair?

Hair.

As the sky brightened, he distinguished the outlines of her behind the sheet. The shape of her body unwinding on the floor behind the veil, under the table. A white shadow. Dead? A slight, peaceful movement in her chest. Not dead. Asleep? After all, when they had first found the palace, she had spent weeks sleeping there, as she used to with her mother, in case a bomb came in the night. Maybe. But not gone.

He stepped back and stumbled away from the door. He thought about running away. He wanted to laugh. He felt guilt grasping his throat and squeezing tight and tighter. And then he suddenly felt warm. The rich, soft note ringing in his ears sang – she stayed!

She must have waited. Could he just turn up now? He had been too long. He could not even explain why. He knew he must, but what would he say?

His feet slowly guided him back to the door, snowflakes decorating his shoulders and eyelashes like jewellery. His hand almost on the latch.

Steps. Cracks. Crackles of frozen weeds breaking. One set of feet. Two. Ten. Making the woodland scream like crickets.

They had found him. He was lost.

He stumbled across the terrace. Eyes in a fever, scanning every crevice of the dead garden. Searching for refuge. For a hiding place. He dragged his body beyond the edge of the terrace, through the empty flower beds. He ducked behind the short wall that bound their old home and pressed himself against the frozen soil. Curled up, heaving, he held his own legs to keep them from shaking, his cheek pressed into the dirt. The soil sneaked in behind his eyelids. A root dug painfully into his neck. A shiny, black beetle was creeping up from the ground.

They had followed him. He could hear them moving, and the woodland shivered. Hiding in the trees, waiting, no doubt, for him to give up, to surrender, to go back with them.

Leo dared to peek through a gap in the rocks; the rocks they had stacked up one summer to keep the snakes from nesting in the garden, terrorising the foxes they had come to love. The terrace looked frozen, waiting, still pale blue. A trap in disguise, made tempting by sweet colours. And it struck him then, in a swing of terror, that his own brown hat lay in the middle of the floor, already wearing miniscule flakes of icy snow.

You've hidden again, haven't you, Leo.

Leo did not move. He turned to the insect slowly, ready, yielding, watching its antennas quiver on its grim, black head and he heard the beetle's words without a hint of surprise.

Always running away. You gutless, feeble, sneezy little child.

Leo whispered, no, I am here, I came back.

Oh, but you left. You left her alone. You didn't even explain why. You hid your thoughts from her all those years. You pulled the ground from under her feet without a hint of shame, like a wimpy, vile insect. The beetle crawled towards his face, an inch from his nose, clicking its pincers in judgement. *Can you hear them now? Hear them. Fear them. They're hiding in the woods. They want you to come out. They're here to execute you. Deserter. You hid. You led them to her. Deserter. Traitor. Dead.*

Leo squeezed his eyes shut, wishing himself somewhere else, away, away. Somewhere without soldiers hiding in the trees. Somewhere he had not run away from. Somewhere warm. Somewhere summer.

Leo the impostor. The liar. The soldier. The beetle bit every word with a click of its horrid wings. *Coward. Snake. Bastard.*

It continued to hiss sharply in his face, while Leo squeezed his eyes tighter, while he wished himself away, away. While he thought of the garden when the days were green and the light ambered.

Remember Sam?

Leo opened his eyes suddenly, nauseously, terrified. No.

Yes, you do.

No, no. I don't, I don't.

Lies. He helped you cross the train tracks in that town, what was it called? He helped you get through and when you saw the soldiers chasing you, you tripped him over and left him to be taken. Don't you know they executed him? Right there in the snow. On the road right where you let him fall. It's what they do to deserters, don't you know? It's what they'll do to you. But you couldn't watch, could you. You hid. You ran away.

Leo wheezed, no, I had to get home, I had to find her.

The beetle poked his nose with its pincers, hissing, *Lies. She never wants you back. She's forgotten you. You hid from her. You told her you hated war and then you volunteered. And then you left her. And you fought.* It snapped. *Killed.* It ticked. *You burned. And why? Do you even know? Did you even care? And now you've led them to her. Spit. Rot. Die.*

Leo hid his nose in the frozen soil, choking on the whimper building in his throat, the beetle snapping his pincers closer and closer.

It was revenge, wasn't it? Your father, your brothers, your friends were dead long ago. Your first home razed to the ground when you were a child. Drop. Dead. Buried. Your old life had been in ashes for ever.

The beast slowly crawled on his nape, gripping Leo's dark skin with coarse, convulsing legs.

You wanted to even the score. You joined the fire that burned the homes of other people. Had you forgotten you used to be other too? Murderer. Pointless. You had a choice. You volunteered. You laugh, you mock, you scorn those who couldn't run away. Those who were called to war, who were drafted like Sam. Those who had to burn, who had to kill, who didn't have a choice. You never told him, did you? He never knew that you'd volunteered, that you'd run into the arms of war. You were always just a deluded boy. She begged you, she held you. She knew you would rot. She was right. Traitor. Die.

Yes! he cried. She was right. Murderer and traitor and weak. I am I am I am.

A creak. A breath. A step too soft.

Leo looked at the terrace through the gap in the rocks. Her features came back to him as he saw her, even as time had changed her face, even as they were not quite children anymore. The snow had stopped. The fold under her chin was not as full, her hair was shorter now. The bow of her full lips was pale, creased by small lines at the sides. Her freckles were the same. To him she still looked warm. She had always felt like summer.

He murmured, Polly.

Here she goes looking for your hat, Leo. So kind of you to lure her out for them.

No, thought Leo, not her, not now. I am here, I am home.

He listened to the sound of her bare feet on the frosty floor, as she walked out, as she bent to reach his hat. He watched as she held it in her hands like she would a wounded bird.

The soldiers flew on her in a moment, running out of the trees. The march of the ranks abandoned, their brown uniforms blurred into one, like one fist falling to send the snow up in tidal waves, the tips of their rifles clanging like wind chimes.

And they struck her down. And they beat her face. And they tied her hands. And they laughed and they jeered and they cheered as she bled.

Leo whimpered and cried, choking his misery with the dirt, clasping his throat with his hands. They can't hear me, they can't hear me.

You're still going to hide, aren't you. Even as you feed her life to them, you're still going to cower here with me. Vile. Dirt. Stain.

Please, Leo cried to himself, please go, follow, find her, get her back. But his legs were ice. His heart was crumbling like chalk. His chest had stopped drawing in breath.

He watched frozen, horrified, as they loaded her onto their cart and drove her away, away. And still, as they disappeared in the distance, his grief took on a hint of relief. Because they had left. Because they had not found him.

Pale blue. Charcoal. The pearly white of the snow. Deep red. The blood had stained the white floor like a bunch of mushed grapes.

The beetle crawled down from his nape while Leo stared at the drops, dazed. As if he could still see the gash on her cheek. Her pleading eyes. Thick blood painting her face red, trickling down her chin and on the floor.

It hissed. *The snow must have looked just like this after you left Sam to die.*

Leo turned his back to the beetle. He turned towards the tall glass door and marched inside. A fury had started dancing around his head. He found the poker just where they had always kept it. In a fold of the fireplace that once gleamed familiar and now rested, cold.

Through the door, he could see the red splashes. He could see where her cheek had been. He marched outside and without faltering he lifted his arm, raised the poker high above his head, and struck, struck, struck the mudstone floor. He struck Polly's blood, he squashed the wretched beetle until yellow pus oozed from its belly. And then he struck it more and more and more, until the stone split and water poured out from the pipes underneath, washing the blood and the snow and the dead husk of the beetle away.

Leo used to be tender. Leo used to be sweet. He used to feel younger with every coming spring. His fingers could tie strings into soft dresses and grass into pages.

He dropped the poker and stood up straight and, as water flowed over his feet and got in his shoes, he looked to the garden. He looked to the edge of the woodland where the trees opened to give way to what remained of the grass, once purple with heather, now greyed. And he saw the ghosts of Polly and himself passing before his eyes, airy and glittering, sweet. He played the chase of their childhood games in his memory and he chose to remember her and to forget his crimes.

For the second time in his life, he moved to make his home inside the palace. This time, he was alone.

There's Something Wrong With Gran

Kirsten Provan

I can't remember the exact moment I realised Gran might be a wee bit abnormal. The woman was always eccentric. We were all used to it. The electric-green, cat-eye spectacles. Her powdery, lilac curls like a sunset cloud. The draping, leopard-print shawl. How she was all hahaha, mouth wide, showing even the brown teeth at the back. The red, heeled sandals that *click-clack*ed when she scurried across the linoleum floor. Her cats deid as doornails. She was never really one for being low-key. Walking around, *click-clack-click-clack*, like the lovechild of Dame Edna and George of the Jungle. Watch out for that tree, possums. But still, despite all that, I'd never really considered her odd. She was just like hiccups, something weird that couldn't be explained. And, now more than ever, she had a habit of popping up unexpectedly.

But, you know, to be fair to the woman, she's the reason I remember our childhood so fondly. And so well. Largely because I've got her constantly loitering by my side, shrilly reminding me of the good times, how bloody lucky we were to have a Gran like her. The twice-cooked toast. Biscuit toast we called it, thinking we were pure knowledgeable. What a treat. Done under the grill, of course. Gran wouldn't do it any other way. There was something shifty about toasters, she said, how they'd managed to seamlessly infiltrate our lives, with their fancy dials and meaningless settings. But we all knew it was really the *BRING!* when it popped that she was afraid of. OH, HELP MA BOAB! she would screech, clutching frantically at her chest, like she was doing one of her old disco dances. And we would titter and chitter from our hiding place underneath the kitchen table, copying every move of her juddering jive. *Tehehehe.* Lying

practically on top of each other, shielded by the tablecloth, watching her red, heeled sandals *click-clack-click-clack* across the linoleum; it was pure toe-tapping panic. And I remember, too, when she rudely pushed that toaster back into Mum's reluctant arms. Just give it to the charity shop, Jane, Gran had fussed. They're always looking for fancy goods like this. And next year, don't buy me something so modern. In my day, we didn't need all these gadgets and gizmos, ta very much.

Mum never did get round to throwing that toaster away, but we hid it out of sight so as not to incense the old woman. All the while, not one of us had the guts to stand up and tell her that toasters were around long before she was. So we crawled out from under the table, all sorrysorrysorry, and told her she was the greatest thing since toasted bread. We couldn't run away fast enough. *Click-clack-click-clack* as she scuttled after us with a tea towel.

Anyway, as I was saying, she always toasted the toast twice. God help anyone who tried to stop her. Once for the colour: bronzed, like a penny. And then a second time, once the butter had been smothered on, to achieve the perfect level of crispiness. It had to be the proper French butter in the gold-foil packets, not any of that spreadable, plastic tub nonsense. It was non-negotiable; anyone who suggested otherwise faced being written out of the will by the time tea was over. And though the biscuit toast had to be crispy, it couldn't be *too* crispy for Gran, lest, Heaven forbid, she chipped one of her precious, yellowing veneers. While we mocked it at every opportunity, it *was* decent toast to be fair, and none of us were up for living without it. These days, every time I traipse past that battered toaster, shoved unceremoniously on one of the many charity piles that now line the halls of Gran's house, she never fails to remind me about the biscuit toast and how we terrorised her. Pot, kettle, Gran.

Och, Gran loved us, how could she not? Sometimes she just couldn't quite remember the reasons why. Our relentless banter grated on her. She was constantly having to remind herself why she liked having us around. Why she let Mum dump us on her every evening after school and every day during the summer holidays. Six long weeks of us and on and on we'd titter and chitter, even when she was in the living room, lying spread-eagled on her favourite chair, a warm flannel over her eyes, blue mascara tracks like bulbous veins down her cheeks. Her ice-cold gin, strong as anything, left rings on the coffee table but she turned the big light off so she couldn't see them and blared her remedial Mozart to drown us out. *Da dum da dum da.* Or however it went. She often joked that the doctor gave her music on prescription to help her cope with our patter. To which we asked: what about the gin? Ignoring us, she moved her wrinkled fingers in time with the music. Mouth agape, muttering pure nonsense. Stifled giggles behind sticky hands. Even the Grim Reaper couldn't stop her talking. *Hahaha.* Chortle. Chortle. She'd annoy him so much, he'd turn his boat around in the middle of the Styx and bring her back. Maybe that's what happened.

But still, no matter how much of a riot we were, Gran always came through with the biscuit toast. And alongside it, if you were really, very lucky, you might get a perfectly boiled egg too. CRACK! Oooooh, look how orange that one is. My one's proper yellow, that's rarer. My one was purple but I ate it before yous could see. Liar! Liar! Gran, he's telling lies again! And repeat with the flannel, favourite chair, strong gin, and the dulcet tones of Uncle Mozart. Perhaps we were the ones the Grim Reaper would get sick of. Perhaps it was a family affliction. Perhaps, perhaps, perhaps.

It wasn't just the biscuit toast that made us love Gran. It was also those wee ramekins, filled up with Maltesers, shoved hurriedly into our pawing hands as soon as Mum had scarpered. We'd properly scran them. Far too quickly, every time. Recently, I've started to wonder if Gran gave us all that food just to shut us up, just so she could forget we were there, if only for a wee while, but then she still had to listen to the *CRUNCH!* and the *SLURP!* and the *EW THAT'S SO MINGING!*

We always came back from Gran's house stuffed to the very brim, our breathing shallow and painful. Puffing and panting like we were already old and decrepit ourselves. On the worst days, even the walk around the corner proved too far and we'd bundle into Gran's spare room and fall into a collective food coma. Nowadays, when I'm sleeping in there, the loud, floral wallpaper still gives me the boke, but the thought of sleeping anywhere else in the house gives me the absolute fear.

Henry and Cat even loved Gran for non-food-related reasons. It was her makeup, the foundation-caked brushes and the clean, sweet smell of her beloved rouge, that Henry was obsessed with. That boy could spend an age sitting at her vanity, staring wistfully into his blue-mascara-ringed eyes. Pouting his thin, wee lips, the pinkest of pink lipsticks smeared haphazardly across them. It was the *DO NOT DISTURB!* sign he put on the door that made me and Cat cackle.

GET OUT! he'd squeal. I'M PREPARING FOR MY MOST IMPORTANT SHOW YET! YOU *ALWAYS RUIN EVERYTHING!* Hours later, long after we'd got bored of pestering him, Henry would emerge, dolled up to the nines, ready to monologue. The acting wasn't half bad, there was something captivating about the way he skipped around the coffee table, but the makeup was shocking, smeared on as though he'd done it in the dark, with his eyes shut, and his hands tied behind his back. Over the years, he did get better at the application, but with really only Gran's rosy-red cheeks and over-lined lips to learn from, there was never much hope for the poor boy. Still, he loved Gran for letting him play and he loved her even more when, instead of a ramekin full of Maltesers, she once pressed the bubble-gum-pink lipstick into his eager palm.

Wee Cat loved Gran for her stories. She was the only one of us who ever really stuck around to listen. And she liked to lord that over us. How Gran liked her the most; how she knew Gran best because she could recite her stories word for word. After a while, I think she secretly started to get bored with the stories, because they were always the same. And, despite how superior she liked to believe herself, we all knew them. How, when Gran was a girl, all the boys wanted to take her dancing but she would turn them away if they didn't show up on her doorstep with flowers and a sheepish grin. How, on her wedding day, while she was in the dress and everything, Gran had bolted, leaving everyone convinced she was ditching my expectant grandfather, only to return twenty minutes later with a packet of cigarettes under her arm and a sheen of sweat on her brow; she couldn't be expected to get married without a fag first. But by far my favourite of Gran's stories was the time, on her honeymoon, when a thief stole her handbag. She chased the criminal down, pure raging, threw her shoe at him and made him apologise. It was a good story, to be fair. All the vivid details: how fast she could go before the hip replacement, the *click-clack-click-clack* as she ran.

Despite Henry and Cat both loving Gran, they pied her as soon as they got the chance. I was the only one who stayed behind. And somehow, because I stayed, I became the family disappointment. How was that fair? I mean, I was a disappointment for other reasons, like the fact that Henry was now an actor experiencing moderate success on the stage and Cat was a war correspondent for the BBC who, strangely, now called herself Catriona. Little old me, on the other hand, well, I was working as an IT consultant in the basement of a less-than-reputable company and staying permanently at Gran's house, surrounded by cardboard boxes and her frilly furnishings. Moving straight from my childhood bedroom to Gran's spare wasn't exactly my great life plan, but they all took pity on me when they realised I'd do absolutely anything to avoid paying digs. All the same, it wasn't like any of them would jump at the chance to hunker down in a mad old woman's bungalow; I was doing them a favour really.

Living with Gran wasn't so bad. Sure, she was constantly commenting on my job, my love life, my hair, and my more successful siblings who never bothered to visit. But still, it was Gran, and I liked having her around.

If you want the truth, well, I suppose we only started to drift when she began shouting at me, screaming at me, berating me for some minor fault of mine in the middle of the night. It was the howls and the moans and the *WHYYYYYYY!* I could hear her screeches no matter where I was in the house. And it was driving me absolutely doolally. Aye, I'd say it was only when this behaviour started that I had to stop and consider the possibility that she might not be quite right. That she might be, horror of horrors, a wee bit odd. Of course, she'd been dead for years by that point.

The haunting had started out amiably enough. It was all just a bit of fun really. She'd shout that my toast was burning when it wasn't. That my flies were undone when they were perfectly zipped. That someone was at the door when no one had knocked for years. But now, everything was different. *She* was different. She wasn't really Gran anymore, you know? She'd even stopped telling those stories that had filled our childhood, and no one ever saw that coming. We'd always joked that even in death she'd find some way to remind us about her square go with that thief. Turns out, we were wrong. Nowadays, she just sort of wailed. And when she wasn't wailing, she was howling. And when she wasn't howling, she was keening, mostly for herself.

Sometimes, though, the only noise was her hacking smoker's cough, like a retching cat. That was the worst of them all. Once you've heard the sound of dead phlegm, you're changed forever. Trust me.

Honestly, it wasn't a situation I had ever expected to find myself in. Haunted by your own gran. Can you imagine? But it was starting to take its toll. She appeared every day around noon and sat, like always, in her favourite chair, confined for eternity to her garish Chintz recliner. It annoyed me for some reason that she was just permanently there. But, I mean, it was the chair she died in, so I guess I didn't really want to sit there anyway. Still, it was the other things that were doing my head in, the caterwauling late at night, the dampness in the air no matter how high I cranked up the heating. Folk at work were starting to notice the shadows under my eyes, the constant bouts of flu, how jumpy I had become.

I promise I considered all options before finally deciding on my plan. Those sleepless nights gave me a lot of time to plot against her. I didn't *want* to do it but the memory of biscuit toast was just not strong enough to cancel out the dislodging of mucus from beyond the grave. So, I chucked the chair.

I did it in the morning because I didn't want her stare boring into me as I betrayed her. I'm not going to lie to you, the chair was proper heavy. Course it was – it contained Gran's entire life and soul. I tried to lift it, but after a good ten minutes of a lot of straining and not a lot of progress, I resorted to dragging it, knowing she'd give me a good skelp for marking her cream carpets. Lugging Gran's chair down the hall, past those endless charity shop piles that I could never be bothered to sort, some of that old mischievousness awoke inside me. Phantom *click-clacks* followed me to the front door; that familiar tittering and chittering bubbled up from somewhere deep in my chest. With relish, I booted the recliner down the drive. It made one god-awful *SQUEAK!* and *SQUEAL!* as it slid towards the kerb. Typical of Gran to try and get the last word in, eh? *Tehehehe* I could almost hear Henry and Cat snickering.

Afterwards, it was like a leopard-clad weight had been lifted. No one else in the family knew about Gran's ghoulishness; Henry and Cat were always too busy to talk and Mum never really saw her as anything but free childcare. So, the house was mine; no more Gran riding shotgun. I idled in the hall, not really paying attention, too consumed by my own victory and all that. Suddenly entranced by my warped, smug reflection in the stainless steel of Gran's nemesis, I found myself picking up the discarded toaster, fantasies about dropping it off at the local Oxfam on the way to work swam before my eyes. But then there was that all-too-familiar sound of Gran clearing her old, dead throat. The wet, choking gurgle of her swallow. *GULP!* I dropped the toaster. Crumb pandemonium.

I spun around slowly, peeking through the crack in the living room door. The chair was back, in the spot it had always been, and Gran was perched on the end of it, outrage etched across her dead face. She smiled slowly, *SCREEEEEEEECH!* went her overly-rouged, rubber cheeks as she showed me her yellowing veneers.

'That wasn't very nice, was it?'

Fuck. That was exactly what she said to the thief right before she threw her shoe at him.

this is your final boarding call

Adam Vaughn

There is a hidden train in the Old Town that can take the living to the Land of the Dead. Upon entering St. Cuthbert's Kirkyard, one must knock on the tomb of an ancestor, and wait. If there is no reply, there is no ride. But if one shall feel, not hear, a KNOCK-KNOCK-KNOCK deep within, where body meets soul, passage is not only permitted … it is required.

It's as simple as that. It's as simple as dying. Shall we begin? Good. Let us start with…

The Fortune of Finn

Mum died. That's how these things start, right? The death. No sense avoiding it, Death didn't avoid her. We're taught in school about all sorts of famous deaths, like Princess Di, literally in her name. Not that Mum was famous or anything. Not really, anyway. She was a teacher, fame means you're in clarty magazines. *Princess Di was* Mum always said. *Don't let me end up in some hoor magazine* Mum always said. *I don't want to go like her* Mum always said. They still shared the same fate. We all do.

Prince and princess, king and queen ... titles, titles ... get tae fuck. We had this bollocks career survey and even there, titles, titles, this bubble for boy and this bubble for girl, draw within the circle, get in your bubble, *get in the fuckin' hoose the now, 'lass',* titles, titles.

Guess that brings this to me. *Hiiii,* I'm Finn. I was told I'd been named after the Irish word for 'fair', which makes sense given my grades, but turns out my parents named me after *Huckleberry* before realising how racist that book is. They probably would have named me differently if they knew how big of a pain in the arse I'd be. Mum embraced it, buying me tattered Bowie or Blondie tees from the charity shops, helping me skive school for a quick daunder around Portobello, or sneaking me sips of her mulled cider at every possible chance. Dad, well, took the other approach. He overworked to compensate for all of his under-ness; his underperforming as a father, his underestimating my abilities because *some wee fuckin' dickhead is gonna try n pop a kid in'ya the second yer tits pop,* and his underwear, which he struts around the flat in – it's so embarrassing.

I was used to death by the time she went. Dad's dad went first. He taught me that life could be *pure dead brilliant* if one wanted it. Mum's dad went next. He showed me how to hang with the lads, who I get on with better, and cheated in basically every game that didn't matter – unlike my dad who cheats on everything that does. Mum's step-mum (never knew her mum-mum), who wasn't total shite, pushed for naming me Finn as Mark Twain was her favourite; so yeah, she was kinda racist and lived longer. Dad's mum is a dafty and's the lone survivor and she reads *The Sun* and no one talks to her. Point being, the shit ones always live in the stories. I lean heavily towards rank, but have a twinge of good that makes what I'm about to do a complete toss-up.

I am going to the Land of the Dead. Let's see if I return.

THE FOOL

0

Mors patet, Hora latet. This is where you are now, my dear. The Fool. The essence of this saying becomes evident when one is ready. Oh you are, huh? Death, not time, will tell. I do sense a strong intuition in you, a sense of beginner's luck that has gotten you this far in life. Yet you are at the precipice of choice. Will this luck take you far enough in what you seek? The Fool does not know but must trust. Do you trust? Do you trust me? Good.

When passage is permitted, the KNOCK-KNOCK-KNOCK of acceptance reverberates within like a second heart. The heartbeat of the departed dead. Once felt, there is no going back. Life and death are diametrically opposed places with no in between. The accepted will find themselves two metres underground, in a coffin made of dirt and decay, where no one can hear their screams. There is no going back. There is only going forward. Into the tunnel. To the train.

I arrived at St. Cuthbert's, pondering what that lavvy heid said, *more pâté hoor latte* or some shite; couldn't even be bothered with the Google translation, the fud. Anyway, Mum's mum-mum, the one I never knew, is a descendent of some eighteenth-century reverend, Vic-Mc-Ar-Someone, who preached or whatever at Cuthbert's and then got buried there. *Put me in the fuckin' dug's scran for all I care* was Dad's response. But this meant that Mum too would one day be buried next to her mum and her great-great-et cetera-granddad of hers. *Braw.* A rare time I actually agree with Dad.

The kirkyard is in disarray these days, and its layout reminds me of a jumble shop with the just-stack-that-on-top and put-that-over-there-mate decisions all over the place, but in this case, it's tombs. I went at night, not to sneak out of the house or anything – who needs to when Dad spends most of his nights in his other flat by work *because I need to be there, Finn* which is code for fucking stupid fucking Tara and her blonde hair and gravity-defying fake tits. They perk upwards like a birdwatcher, the absolute hackit. I suppose they deserve each other. If I had a pound for every time I overheard him say to a mate *if I can touch them they're real* or Tara say to one of hers *a wee prick for a big bank account* I'd, well … well, I'd still be a skint teenager but like, with some money which would be nice.

When mine came that sorta changed things for me, and not just Dad's ever-increasing paranoia about *pricks*. There are days where I'm happy to have them, but other times, when I look in the mirror – that thing that reveals who you really are and fuck-all otherwise – where I just can't. Like, I wish I could just open the wardrobe and zip up another flesh outfit; to have pecs instead of tits, a beard instead of none for this dreich weather, to have a penis ... like, on me, not in me (not that I've had either experience, boys are *bawheids*). I just feel so lost in this body I'm living in. That's why I'm okay with whatever happens. Because how can something so complicated and yet so simple like life, like death, be so binary? I feel my existence too, like my gender, is somewhere in between. And that somewhere in between is the only person who ever even tried to see the real me, not the one trapped in the mirror.

Rain fell (thanks, Scotland) in the creepy kirkyard (thanks, Scotland) as my boots stuck and unstuck themselves in the sludge (thanks, Scotland). Weird humidity, wind that seemed to build and never crescendo, sideways rain like the weather's blootered and pissing on a bin. Nothing smells better to me than rain-hitting-decomposing-earth (it doesn't smell like piss, I swear). More like Life & Death coming soon from Calvin Klein; this is why no one wants to hold my hand.

Echoes and shadows and the unexplainable bounced in all directions, my ears spinning this way and that like a frightened deer. Each step brought its own little surprise: decaying leaf piles, crunching gravel, sticks threatening to puncture my dilapidated boots. Wind howled suggestions that encouraged my mind to keep playing its little games – trees became monsters, tombstones became zombies – further reminding me not to trust myself.

I kept walking forward, looking over my shoulder, ready for whatever hunts deer to attack. That's when it got me. A ghost tripped me over a cobble and I tasted muck -- really I'm just clumsy. Lights from the castle bled ominously across the sky as I looked up, certain I would die. My phone torchlight was no match for the swirling clouds and ceaseless pelting; outside was boggin'. *Bring your brolly, Finn.* Piss off, Dad.

Covered in mud, I realised that I hadn't been to the kirkyard since Mum's funeral, when I was also caked with mud 'cause again, 'ghosts' (or clumsiness). But the cards said to go. *The Fool does not know but must trust.* Well, here I am, trusting this Latin-gibberish-speaking, self-proclaimed 'witch', a five quid tarot reading from someone named Charon (*it's pronounced Karen*) Boatman (*no, it's Boooootman*). She claimed to be the reincarnation of Charon, the ferry*wo*man to Hades, but in reality she's a complete dobber with an eejit face and an eejit shop in an eejit city. Oh, and really, really good hearing. And yet, some part of me knows that I must do this. For Mum.

Anyway, I mean, I could have either just puttered back and forth at home, alone, dwelling on my dad 'at work' with the woman he'd already moved on to before Mum moved on to the other side, on how I spent half my weekly pocket money on some mince tarot reading, on the fact that the last words I'd said to her were *I wish you'd die* – or do this, go snooping in a kirkyard, so, yeah. Best not to dwell in the dwelling; wonder if homes are called dwellings for that reason? I also wonder if everyone actually gets one wish in their lifetimes but never knows when it will happen, and that was the wish that came true for me.

Doors open, bags drop, feet stomp, doors slam.

It's nothing.

It's obviously something.

I don't want to talk about it.

I wish you would.

Knock-knock-knock.

I wish you'd tell me what's wrong, Finn.

I wish you'd …

Time later, she did. An accident. No one's fault. 'Cept for maybe the AirPods.

I'd *finn*ished off my mum. Not really 'fair' if you ask me.

A cold what's-that blew on my nape. I spun around. It felt like the night was watching itself, aware of all comings and goings, aware that I should be going too. My shadow, on the tomb of Reverend McVicar, eyeballed me, a hollow mirror, a me sucked away from myself into the void of death. Leaves funnelled upwards, blasting me in the face like Garry Baird's older brother said he'd do to me (everyone's a cunt).

Where was my mum's tomb? I meandered through the yuck, my eyes squinting through the pelting rain, scanning the tombstones with my iPhone. Headlights from a passing maintenance truck illuminated the nothingness where there should be a something-ness. Her tomb was gone.

I attempted to move closer, but it seized me, whatever it was, from within my body. I wanted so desperately to run, to move, to do literally anything, but couldn't. The ground trembled, triggering my vertigo, the city tossed on 'tumble dry' mode. My heart kicked into high gear as the wind spoke, screaming its haunting nonsense into my ears as my eyes blurred; the castle lights washed over the kirkyard, red with warning, red like Christmas gone wrong, bloody, mangled, menacing. Sharp eyes radiated from the tombstones, closing in on me, red blending with red, eyes that reminded me of that day during first year – last year – when Mum died, and everyone stared, stared, stared.

And that's when I felt it.

KNOCK

KNOCK

KNOCK

I hadn't even knocked on the tombstone but still I felt it, a heartbeat within a heartbeat, somewhere within me. A sense that I was somewhere in between somewhere, something in between something, me and myself, life and death.

The it, whatever it was, snatched my voice, my body, me. Ever so slowly, I slipped into the confines of my mum's missing tomb, body squelching through leaves and grass and mud and soil. Dirt rode up my breeks and shirt and soon filled my mouth. I took a breath, clogged with grit, hoping it wouldn't be my last.

DESIRE · OBSESSION · FEAR · SHADOW

THE DEVIL

XV

The Devil: This is where you've been, Finn. Caged in yourself. Common for your age, what thirteen? Almost fourteen, my mistake. You're a big girl now. Oh you'll know when I'm patronising you. Besides, I'm just a, what did you mutter when you entered my shop? 'A coddled white girl who wasn't told no enough'? Didn't think I heard that, huh? It's okay, I get it. You're young, you're clever. You must know everything. Everything about who you are? That's what I thought. See, the cards never lie. Shall I continue?

When one boards the Train of Last Passage, one should be aware that oftentimes, the train is fully booked. Death is always selling tickets. Business is always booming. And of course, as always, all sales are final. There are no stops. There are only one-way tickets. And the train always arrives on time. You have but one choice, to stay or go, when you hear the whistle blow.

I woke to the same glow of the castle, underground, in a coffin of sorts, the walls not wood but instead compacted soil. My screams would go unheard, I was sure of it, but that didn't stop me from letting them loose.

Mind and breathe, Finn. Okay, okay, fine. In and out, in and out, yes good. Good. I was still alive. I was unhurt. I was on my back in a tomb made of dirt, but still alive. From behind my feet, a faint medley of reds glimmered from what appeared to be a small, endless tunnel no wider than an air vent like ones in our school gym. Turning about posed a challenge, but what else was I supposed to do? *Stay put, Finn, until I get back with some ice cream. It won't be long.* Well, it has been long, Mum.

The crawl was cumbersome, like this long lift ride I once had with my Dad and I had to fart but it was just him and he'd yell at me *for fuck's sake, Finn.* Like then, there too I was clenching every part of my body trying to make it through successfully.

I emerged in the station, two metres up from the platform, slotted in some sieve of a wall in an endless corridor with endless holes and endless arrivals. Flames from torches illuminated the dead and their funeral-makeup faces as they climbed into the station of creaking wood floors and gold accents everywhere, floral wallpaper with hypnotising apple trees that shined and tempted my empty belly and empty soul. Awestruck, mouth agape, dumbfounded. A dummy with a bunch of dead. It was like a really good Halloween party, like the ones adults have, when Mum would say *I think they're a little confused* when really her friend was drunk and I chored enough ciders until they were gien me the boke all over Dad's office. I felt absolutely reekin' and scared and knew I shouldn't be there.

With a bendy pivot – thank you, gym class – and a quick shimmy, I clambered down to the platform with a toddler's grace. There it was, that same red light, this time shining from the train in little haloes from frilly, green lamps. The inside of the train looked like some ageing cabin in some place like Fort William or Skye or wherever we used to take holiday retreats to *recharge the family spirit*. Tartan-green carpeting and crooked wooden booths completed the mood. Broken in and worn oot. Clearly business was booming, like Charon said.

I noticed a sign hanging over the platform:

Mors patet, Hora latet.

There, again. Her words. Fitting a dead language is used to greet the dead.

A whistle blew as I approached, my legs carrying me to the train doors on their own. Yet some part of me no longer wanted to be there – the apparent binary-ness of the decision, to stay or go, seemed wrong. I was just so convinced that nothing, not me, not life and death, could be so exact. A or B, potato pot*aht*o, boy or girl. Well, not me.

That's when she showed up, in a matching maroon suit and tie and double-cream shirt, at the train doors. She – ferrywoman, gatekeeper to the underworld, coddled white girl, in most ways the same except the lighting down here doing wonders for her cheekbones. Charon.

You made it.

What the hell are you doing down here?

My job.

I stared at Charon, bewildered. How could she—

Ticket?

287

You didn't say anything about a ticket.

Charon smirked, like someone excited to tell their waiter the food is cold.

Payment is required.

Well, what else can I pay with?

Your life.

A final whistle blew in that way you just know a thing's final. Charon snatched my arm and dragged me aboard, tossing me onto a nearby bench that reminded me of my granddad's room of books that I would never read. I sat up, thunking my head hard on the table underside, slumping under to the dusty, skin-flaked floor.

Charon stepped off the train as I slowly recovered. She looked up at the platform sign, and back to me. *Death is sure, the Hour obscure.*

The doors shut, despite my best lunge since that one time I half-assed instead of zero-assed gym class.

Charon smiled deviously. *Enjoy your one-way travel.*

I glared at Charon as the train slowly pulled away, and wrote in the condensation of the train's window:

BRB

This is where you are heading to, Finn. Death. Usually I'd say, don't worry, you won't actually die; it's just a part of you that will no longer remain. But this ... no one has ever returned from what you're attempting to do. Not afraid you say? Well that's a rather ... devilish attitude to have.

Upon arrival at Thanatos, capital city of the Land of the Dead, one is greeted by Ankou, Ambassador to the Dearly Departed. Ankou has one horse, one wagon, and one job: get the Dead to their Endings. It's an easy job, as long as everyone who arrives is, of course, dead. If not, Ankou knows how to take care of that too.

The Bell of the Banshee

Bells rang as I arrived in the Land of the Dead. I knew they rang for me – a both, a living amongst the dead, a broken rule, a thing that could not be, a thing that does not exist. Well, that's me. I exist.

It's funny, heading off to the Land of the Dead is the most alive I've ever felt. Well, that and skiving school with Mum. They're kinda the same though, yeah?

I've never given a shit about anything. I've never tried to do anything, to any thing, for anyone. And yet, I must. And I will.

I will find my mum. I will tell her that I wish she was alive. I will tell her that her death never ended up in *some hoor magazine*. I will tell her I'm sorry. I will be proud. I will tell my dad who I am. I will be both.

Let's see if I return.

THE CONTRIBUTORS

Josephine Balfour-Oatts

Following her graduation with a BA(Hons) in Drama from the University of Bristol in 2016, Josephine put down her roots in the field of arts journalism. Her experience as a theatre critic includes editorial roles at digital magazines, A Younger Theatre, and London Box Office, as well as reviews for *Exeunt* and *Miro Magazine*. Previously, Josephine worked as a Senior Bookseller at Waterstones, Covent Garden, managing the store's Theatre and Art sections. Currently based in Leith, Edinburgh, she contributes regularly to *the Times Literary Supplement* as a critic and is pondering a PhD in English Literature.

Rosa Barbour

Rosa Barbour was born in Glasgow in 1993 and has been drawn to prose writing since childhood. She is compelled to write stories featuring realistic and vibrant dialogue, while locating the inherent magic of the everyday. In 2019 her story 'Humanities' was published in *Gutter Magazine*, and in 2020 her story 'Starflower Bloos' was shortlisted for a John Byrne Award. Rosa is also interested in writing dialogue for actors, and since 2016 has been working with a small creative team to develop *Victoria Sponge*, an independently produced short film, shot on location in Scotland and based on her own screenplay.

Daniela Castillo

Dann Castillo is a writer, illustrator, and semi-professional shower singer. Although originally from Mexico, Dann has had the opportunity to work in more than fifteen different countries around the world. She was the scriptwriter for Alexa, Amazon's Virtual Assistant, where she produced dialogues, stories, songs, and poems for the Mexican market. Her blog, TheDreampacker.com, has been featured in the New York Times, and she recently collaborated in an anthology presented at Guadalajara's International Book Festival. Dann loves long walks and short stories, and most of her characters may or may not be based on real people.

Harry Clough

Harry Clough is a keen lover of old and vintage books and recently bought a thirteen-year-old's 's pocket diary from 1941 off eBay because there's nothing cooler than people's diaries and journals. In between running 1744km for charity this year, Harry writes about natural spaces, childhood memories, sunsets, and sunrises (a slight poetic obsession). Retirement to the Lake District or Shetland is his dream, so if you see him in one of those places in forty-years time, you'll know he's made it.

Annie Zihang Diao

Born in China and relocated to Malta, Annie graduated from the University of Malta with a BA degree in English and Chinese. As a writer from a multicultural background, Annie loves to embody different cultural elements in her writing and experiments across various genres – of which her favourite combination is dark humour and horror. Embarked on an MSc in Creative Writing at the University of Edinburgh, Annie is currently working on completing her first novel.

Daniel Dicks

Dan is a twenty-one years old poet from Bristol. He began writing whilst studying English Literature for his undergraduate degree, inspired by his reading of Modernist and Decadent poets and novelists in his second and third years. If he was asked to define his poetry, he might call it love poetry, though 'break-up poetry' might be a more apt description.

Lindsay Evans

Lindsay is a photographer and writer – and a lover of the creative process. Raised in a small town in New Hampshire, she moved to Edinburgh in 2016 and fell in love with the city and its beauty. In life, she plans to take in all the little moments and make them last – likely by immortalising them within a photo.

Margaret Abigail Flowers

Margaret Abigail Flowers is a jack of all genres. Her written work has appeared in *The Interlochen Review*, *The Leland Quarterly*, and *Scintilla Magazine*. Her one-act plays have been produced across the United States, including in New York City and Los Angeles. Her short film "Shen" premiered at the Harlem International Film Festival, where it received the honor of "Top Short", before going on to screen at a dozen international film festivals. After graduating from Stanford University in 2017, she trekked to the Great Northwest in search of the perfect cappuccino. She stands as the 2020-2021 *From Arthur's Seat* Editor-in-Chief and prefers one sugar, two creams.

Becky Grieve

Becky Grieve is a Scottish writer who grew up in the Borders. Becky recently completed her undergraduate degree in English and Scottish Literature at the University of Edinburgh and graduated in June of 2020. She is currently studying a master's course at the University of Edinburgh where she will graduate in November of 2021. Becky has experimented previously with crime fiction, but is currently working on an anthology of contemporary short stories and flash fiction. Becky is avidly enjoying experimenting with her narrative style – even if she does still tend to forget to punctuate her sentences.

Maria Henry

Maria is a fiction writer and visual artist from Manchester. She enjoys writing stories that usually involve ghosts or ghouls and despite studying film for four years, will claim that 80s sci-fi horror is the best genre (the lower the budget, the better the robots). She is often found engaging in overly enthusiastic debates about how she hates capitalism and wishes the Conservatives would go away.

Laura Hiermann

Laura Hiermann is an Austrian writer who graduated from the University of Vienna with a bachelor's degree in English and American Studies and German Philology. She writes short stories in English and German and is currently experimenting with longer forms of creative writing. Her flash fiction has appeared in online magazines and she is currently a part of the *From Arthur's Seat* social media team.

Sarah Hopkins

Sarah Hopkins writes a mixture of literary and young adult fiction. After graduating from Queen Mary University of London in 2017, she went on to work for the university for what felt like centuries. Growing increasingly jealous of all the people studying around her, she quit her 9–5 and went back to school. Anduze is her first published piece.

Kathia Huitron Moctezuma

Kathia is a Mexican writer. She self-published her first poetry book *You.Me.And Our Beautiful Madness* in 2016 and her second book *South* in 2018. Her poems have also been featured in literary magazines such as *Paradox* and *Wanderlust*, as well as poetic anthologies like *The Light Anthology* by the Soap Box Press, and *Poetica* by Bymepoetry. She's currently studying for her master's in Creative Writing at the University of Edinburgh.

Anna Koulouris

Anna graduated from Syracuse University with a dual degree in journalism and Middle Eastern studies and a minor in philosophy. Originally from Syracuse, New York, she has done various work in the Middle East and has spent the last several years in Jerusalem. She loves literary and historical fiction, ancient Greek philosophy, and subjects that concern press freedom and human rights.

Margaret Kroening

Margaret Kroening is a ten-year veteran of the United States Air Force and has worked in Government contracts since enlisting in 2009. At her civilian day job, she researches, sources, prepares, negotiates, and executes a variety of federal contracts, including Research and Development for COVID vaccines. After hours, her alter ego writes and illustrates stories, collects hobbies, enjoys some light vagabonding as well as jumping out of perfectly good planes, and riding her Harley. Her longest running story, *War Against Warlords*, is a series she first devised over twenty years ago. 'Chasing Valor' is the opening chapter to the series' prequel.

Kate Lavelle

Kate is an Edinburgh-based writer, director, and coffee-drinker originally from California. Prior to embarking on the MSc, she worked in theatre, TV/film production, advertising, and casting in Los Angeles and New York City. Her other interests include breakfast tacos, Bushwick dive bars, and *Phantom Thread*.

Elise Le Bihan

Elise Le Bihan grew up in the beautiful pine tree state of Maine. Being French and American, her bilingual upbringing made her sensitive not only to language but also to the way we interact in different cultures. She received her B.A. in Creative Writing from Sarah Lawrence College in New York and studied violin in the professional division of L'École Normale de Musique de Paris. While teaching Creative Writing
at L'École Française du Maine, she encouraged children to write stories about everything from dog pirates to shy zombies. She lives in Paris and is completing her first novel.

Eva Polett Lopez

Born in California and currently based in Edinburgh, Eva Polett Lopez is a writer of LGBT fiction and poetry. They are a graduate of the University of Edinburgh, where they received an MA in Classics and an MSc in Creative Writing. They are thrilled to be a debut contributor and editor for the 2020-2021 publication of *From Arthur's Seat*.

Alexandre Marceau

Alexandre Marceau is a Canadian writer from Montreal. At the confluence of the Saint-François and Massawippi Rivers, while perusing Bishop's University's literary archive, he discovered that literary timelines, much like veins, carry the intertwined stories that foster a region's identity. His written work has appeared in The Mitre, The Inkwell, and Chronicling the Days; he is the 2020-2021 recipient of the Beaverbrook Canadian Foundation Scholarship; and he is the Co-Founder and Fiction Editor for *yolk*, a Montreal-based literary journal. Many of Alexandre's musings stem from his time spent outside, either rock climbing, snowboarding, or running.

Andrea Mejia Amezquita

Andrea Mejía Amézquita is a writer and translator from Mexico City. Her articles have been published on the digital platform Cultura Colectiva, and she has developed stories for Google Arts & Culture. Her debut novel *Los Sueños Más Oscuros* was published in 2019 and reached the top of the Spanish Gothic Fiction novels chart on Amazon in 2020. Her novel has also been presented in government programs and literary festivals for independent authors. She loves cookies and adventures so much she thought it'd be cool to move to the magical Edinburgh amid a worldwide pandemic to write and eat lots of shortbread.

Ceilidh Michelle

Ceilidh Michelle is an author from rural Nova Scotia. Her first novel, *Butterflies, Zebras, Moonbeams*, published by Palimpsest Press, was shortlisted for the Hugh MacLennan Award for Fiction. Her second novel, *The One*, comes out with Douglas & McIntyre in August 2021.

Ceilidh has had work published in *Entropy*, *Long Reads*, *Broken Pencil*, *Matrix Magazine*, *Cactus Press*, and *Lantern Magazine*.

Sam O'Brien

Sam O'Brien is a writer from New Jersey. Her short fiction has appeared in *Tidal Echoes* and *Jenny Magazine*, and she was shortlisted for the 2019 Magic Oxygen Literary Prize. She attended the Summer 2019 session of the Alderworks Artists and Writers Retreat in Dyea,

Alaska. This year, she has had the pleasure of serving as one of the head prose editors for *From Arthur's Seat*, and is an avid runner, hiker, and outdoor adventurer.

Doug O'Hara

Douglas O'Hara may hail from a small town north of Philadelphia, but he calls the world his home. He has hiked volcanoes in Bali, skydived over Byron Bay, and scoured the glow-worm caves in Waitomo, all of which inspire him to forge new paths forward within his stories. After working in Los Angeles, writing and directing several short films, he received his graduate degree in English Literature at the University of Glasgow, hopped on a bus, and pursued another master's in creative writing at the University of Edinburgh. When he is not writing, Douglas spends most of his time woodcarving, reading, video gaming, fishing, or wandering around somewhere in nature, walking-stick in hand and a notebook by his side.

Sarah O'Hara

Sarah is a fiction writer from Lancashire who graduated from Edinburgh with a degree in English Literature. She is now studying her Msc in Creative Writing here and takes most of her inspiration from the short stories of Lorrie Moore and eavesdropping on other people's conversations (coffee also helps).

Jack O'Rawe

Jack is a writer from Belfast, where he studied English Literature at Queens University. He currently lives in Scotland, where he is completing an MSc in Creative Writing at the University of Edinburgh. He is an avid reader of books, and among his favourites are *The Butcher Boy*, *Motherless Brooklyn*, *Written on the Body*, *God's Own Country*, *Hope: A Tragedy*, *The Bell Jar*, *Trainspotting*, *Vernon God Little*, *The Exorcist*, *The Cement Garden*, *True Grit*, and *The Catcher in the Rye* (the list goes on).

Brevin Persike

Brevin has worked shifts at factories, scrubbed oil out of concrete floors, painted walls later to be destroyed, and flipped three-dollar burgers at a fast-food joint, but none of that has struck his fancy. His writing derives much of its inspiration from the woods of northern Wisconsin where he grew up, and the slow-moving life along the Mississippi River that he grew accustomed to during his undergrad. Now, he finds himself in locked-down Edinburgh, wandering through parks and empty streets. His work can be found in *Sierra Nevada Review* and the *Catalyst*.

Kirsten Provan

Kirsten Provan is from Longniddry, just outside Edinburgh. From 2013–2015 she wrote a monthly column for the *East Lothian News* detailing the many great injustices of teenage life and has since continued to write personal essays, including 'The State of Being State-Educated', published in *Level with Me* in September 2020. In the same year, after graduating from the University of Edinburgh, Kirsten decided to move towards writing fiction. Currently, she is working as Trending Culture Editor for *The EDI Magazine*, Prose Editor on *From Arthur's Seat*, and is exploring all things speculative and bizarre on the page.

Ilaria Remotti

Ilaria Remotti is a fiction writer and translator based in Edinburgh. Her poetry was first published in *The Looking Glass Anthology* in 2017. In 2018, she graduated from the University of York with a bachelor's degree in English Literature. She stands as co-Art Director of the 2020–2021 edition of *From Arthur's Seat* and doubles as an illustrator and plant collector.

Samira Safarzadeh

Samira Safarzadeh was born and raised in Armenia to Persian father and Armenian mother. She is currently working on her debut sci-fi novel but writes across all genres. Samira delves into poetry when in love and spends her days sitting in Parisian cafés, playing with her dog Dani, or getting lost in museums.

Sandeep Sandhu

Sandeep Sandhu is a writer whose main aim is to make readers cry (preferably by causing an emotional release, or tears of joy). After five years in marketing, he travelled around the Eastern Hemisphere for a year and a half, before returning to the UK to complete his Creative Writing MSc at the University of Edinburgh, where he currently resides.

Paulina Schaeffer

Paulina Schaeffer is a Berlin-born writer with a passion for the fantastic as well as the mundane. She completed her Bachelor of Arts in English and German Philology at the Freie Universität in Berlin and is part of the Creative Writing MSc cohort 2020/2021 at the University of Edinburgh. For her, storytelling entails the most wonderful experience of building bridges between reality and worlds that are yet to be discovered. If she is not reading or writing, she loves trying out new recipes as well as exploring the outdoors, backpack and tent in tow.

Adam Vaughn

AV is a writer/screenwriter from a small town you've probably never heard of in Connecticut. They have placed in multiple screenwriting competitions (that you've possibly heard of) and produced a few off-beat dark comedies (that you've definitely never heard of). A writer of mostly-zany, often-uncanny stories that deal with identity, purpose, and existence, they really, really, love pizza, Islay whisky, and the anxiety caused by trying to keep houseplants in existence.

Morgan Waas

Morgan Waas is an avid bookworm and certified daydreamer. She has been reading and writing fantasy for as long as she can remember and is always on the lookout for the magic in everyday life. She moved to Scotland in 2016 to pursue an undergraduate degree from the University of Edinburgh, which she received in 2020. Morgan was a proofreader for *From Arthur's Seat*, which marks her first serious publication.

Simon West

Simon West has worked for many years as a teacher and has undertaken the MSc at the University of Edinburgh to pursue and deepen his interest in writing. He has long dabbled in the arts and chairs The Wayfarer Trust, a charitable organisation which seeks to support and inspire artists of all disciplines. He currently lives in Edinburgh with his wife and children and can usually be found in some corner of the local second-hand bookshop. A dog called Arthur and a cat called Willow contribute to his life in ways he might never have known he needed.

Yuqing Zhuge

Yuqing Zhuge is a member of the 2020–2021 Creative Writing MSc cohort at the University of Edinburgh.

Lightning Source UK Ltd.
Milton Keynes UK
UKHW010735220922
409267UK00002B/412